GLENCOE

The American Journey

Unit Resources

The Americas: Worlds Meet

The First Americans

Exploring the Americas

Colonial America

Growth of the Thirteen Colonies

McGraw Hill Glencoe

Book Organization

Glencoe offers resources that accompany *The American Journey* to expand, enrich, review, and assess every lesson you teach and for every student you teach. Now Glencoe has organized its many resources for the way you teach.

How This Book Is Organized

Each Unit Resources book is divided into unit-based resources and chapter-based resources. A description of each of the many unit and chapter activities available to you in this book can be found on page v.

All unit-based resources appear at the beginning. Although you may choose to use the specific activities at any time during the course of unit study, Glencoe has placed these resources up front so that you can review your options.

Chapter-based resources follow the unit materials. These activities are directly tied to their chapter and/or section and should be used during the course of chapter study.

A Complete Answer Key

A complete answer key appears at the back of this book. This answer key includes answers for all activities in this book in the order in which the activities appear.

The McGraw·Hill Companies

McGraw Hill Glencoe

Send all inquiries to:
Glencoe/McGraw-Hill
8787 Orion Place
Columbus, OH 43240-4027

ISBN: 978-0-07-880596-7
MHID: 0-07-880596-1

Printed in the United States of America.

1 2 3 4 5 6 024 12 11 10 09 08

Table of Contents

The Americas: Worlds Meet

The First Americans

Exploring the Americas

Colonial America

Growth of the Thirteen Colonies

To the Teacher

The American Journey Classroom Resources

Glencoe's Unit Resources are packed with activities for the varying needs of students. Included are the following activities:

Citizenship and Decision-Making Activities

These activities are designed to involve students in grassroots community projects. These service learning projects help students understand how history affects their own lives on a daily basis.

Economics and History Activities

These interdisciplinary activities give students an understanding of the impact of economics on history. Applied to current situations, students are familiarized with economic terms and principles.

Reading Skills Activities

These reinforcement activities correspond to the reading skill lessons presented in each unit opener of the student textbook. The activities allow students to gain additional practice at such reading skills as monitoring, making inferences, and summarizing.

American Literature Readings

These readings provide students with the opportunity to read literature by or about people who lived during different historical periods. Each selection is preceded by background information and a guided reading suggestion, and followed by comprehension and critical thinking questions.

Enrichment Activities

These activities introduce students to challenging content that is related to the information in the student textbook. Enrichment activities help students develop a broader and deeper understanding of history and the community.

Interpreting Political Cartoons

These activities provide students with the opportunity to explore history through serious fun called satire. Students will analyze the cartoons for various methods used in revealing satire such as caricature, symbolism, metaphor, irony, sarcasm, and stereotyping.

Content Vocabulary Activities

These review and reinforcement activities help students master unfamiliar content terms used in the student textbook. The worksheets provide visual and kinesthetic reinforcement of vocabulary words.

Academic Vocabulary Activities

Knowledge of academic terms can significantly boost students' comprehension of academic texts. These activities teach word parts, word relationships, grammar, and other lexical information about academic terms.

Primary Source Readings

These activities allow students to "see" history through the eyes of those who witnessed events and participated in cultural movements. Each selection is preceded by an introduction and a guided reading suggestion and is followed by questions that require students to analyze and interpret the material.

Writing Skills Activities

These activities help students develop and practice writing skills. Skills such as brainstorming, outlining, learning sentence structures, using sensory details, and writing essays are applied to historical concepts.

Social Studies Skills Activities

These activities allow students to practice their critical thinking and social studies skills. At times, activities extend information in the text and can also apply to real world situations. These activities will help students develop skills needed to understand new situations and content.

Differentiated Instruction Activities

These activities give you an opportunity to differentiate your instruction, addressing the different types of learners in your classroom. Teaching strategies address these differentiated learning styles: English Language Learners, Advanced Learners, Below Grade Level, Logical/Mathematical, Verbal/Linguistic, Visual/Spatial, Kinesthetic, Auditory/Musical, Interpersonal, and Intrapersonal.

Critical Thinking Skills Activities

Critical thinking skills are important to students because they provide the tools to live and work in an ever-changing world. These activities show students how to use information to make judgments, develop their own ideas, and apply what they have learned to new situations.

Geography and History Activities

These activities provide students with the opportunity to analyze and interpret historical maps. Students are required to practice using geography skills as an aid to understanding history.

Linking Past and Present Activities

These activities help students recognize the link between the past and the present and understand how the past relates to the present. For example, exploring the changes in information technology from the printing press to computerized desktop publishing will help students realize the past is a prologue to what is present in today's world.

Time Line Activities

These activities reinforce the dates of major events in world history and help students learn the chronological order of those events. Students also see how events occur concurrently in different parts of the world and/or are interrelated.

School-to-Home Connection Activities

These activities contain information and activities that students and their families/caregivers can do at home to reinforce an understanding of geography. They are intended to give parents easy materials to help their children with chapter lessons.

Reteaching Activities

These activities may be used for remediation or reinforcement. A variety of activities enable students to visualize the connections among facts in their textbook. Graphs, charts, lists, tables, and concept maps are among the many types of graphic organizers used.

Guided Reading Activities

These activities focus attention on key information and enable students to make appropriate connections among the facts they encounter in the student textbook. They also provide help for students who are having difficulty comprehending the textbook or who would benefit from a review of the material.

The Americas: Worlds Meet

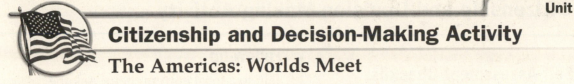

Unit

Citizenship and Decision-Making Activity

The Americas: Worlds Meet

Entrepreneurship—The Foundation of Our Economy

Why It Matters

The era of exploration in the 1500s and 1600s led to our modern economic system of capitalism. Entrepreneurs are important to this system. They are the businesspeople who provide products and services to fulfill needs within our society.

Background

Entrepreneurs combine money, ideas, raw materials, and labor to make goods or provide services. They are motivated by profits. Successful entrepreneurs have a thorough understanding of their chosen business and are willing to take financial risks to make money. They have the ability to see a need in the market, and they develop the products or services that will fill that need.

Questions to Consider

Directions: Answer the questions below on a separate sheet of paper.

1. **Explaining** Refer to your textbook. What motivated investors and explorers in the 1500s and 1600s during the era of exploration?

2. **Analyzing** How do entrepreneurs help our economic system today?

3. **Listing** Who are some famous entrepreneurs today?

Your Task

You will investigate entrepreneurship in your community and will simulate starting a new business.

How to Do It

Work in small groups. Think of ways to participate in the creation of a new business. Follow the steps below.

1. What type of business might be needed in your community? Choose a type of business you want to start and give it a name.

2. Create a plan for starting your business. Use the table on the next page to help your group write a plan for your business.

3. Give an oral presentation to the class about your business.

> ## Did You Know?
>
> In 1872 Elijah McCoy, the son of former slaves, invented a lubricator for steam engines. Imitations became available, but engineers asked specifically for Mr. McCoy's device because of its reliability. Thus, "the real McCoy" became a popular phrase indicating that a product is genuine.

Citizenship and Decision-Making Activity (continued)

Self-Assessment Checklist

Assess your business and marketing plan using the checklist below:

- ☐ We chose a business that fits a need in our community.
- ☐ We wrote a summary of our goals.
- ☐ We wrote a complete list of our products and services.
- ☐ We described our competition and customers in detail.
- ☐ We established positions in the company.
- ☐ We wrote a thorough financial plan.

Follow-up

Talk to a local entrepreneur. Ask the following questions:

1. How did you decide what type of business to open?

2. What is your biggest challenge?

3. What advice would you give to a new entrepreneur?

Writing a Business and Marketing Plan	
Step	**Explanation**
1. Write a company summary.	In a paragraph, list what you want to accomplish with your business.
2. Describe your products or services.	Write four or five sentences describing your products or services. What need will you fill in your community?
3. Describe your market.	Describe the type of people who will buy your products or services. How will you let them know what you have to sell?
4. Describe your competition.	Make a list of businesses that will be your competition. How will your product or service differ?
5. Describe your business structure.	What positions will exist within your company? Who will be the president? Who will sell your product or service?
6. Write a financial plan.	Make a list of items you will need and estimate how much they will cost. Describe how much you expect to charge for your product or service.

Economics and History Activity

The Americas: Worlds Meet

The Colonial Slave Trade

"We hold these truths to be self-evident, that all men are created equal, that they are endowed by their Creator with certain unalienable Rights . . ." These words appear in the Declaration of Independence. Yet in spite of these statements supporting equality, many American colonists engaged in the buying and selling of enslaved people.

Enslaved Africans first arrived in the colonies in the early 1600s. Mercantilism led to high demands for sugar, rice, tobacco, and cotton. Products sent from the colonies to the home country could be sold in Europe for high profits. Enslaved Africans filled the endless demand for the cheap and plentiful labor supply needed to produce these goods. By 1750, more than 200,000 enslaved Africans were living in the colonies.

Common trade routes resembled a triangle and came to be called the triangular trade.

Ships from Europe exchanged goods for enslaved people in Africa. Ships took the enslaved people to the West Indies, where they were sold. They were then taken to the Americas and sold.

One of the most important products of the American South was cotton. Cotton was a labor-intensive crop—it required many people to grow and harvest it. Thus, the economy of the large cotton plantations came to depend on slave labor. The Southern economy grew through the importation of enslaved Africans and through an increase in the exportation of cotton.

In 1808 Congress made it illegal to import enslaved Africans into the United States, but it did not entirely stop the slave trade. Soon traders found new overland routes into the country through Texas and Florida.

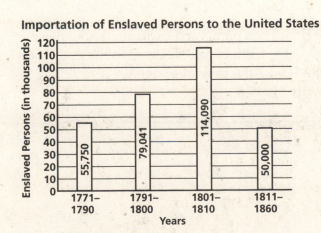

Importation of Enslaved Persons to the United States

Enslaved Persons (in thousands)

Years	
1771–1790	55,750
1791–1800	79,041
1801–1810	114,090
1811–1860	50,000

Source: American University, Washington, DC, 2001.

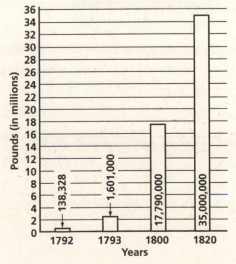

Exportation of Cotton

Pounds (in millions)

Years	
1792	138,328
1793	1,601,000
1800	17,790,000
1820	35,000,000

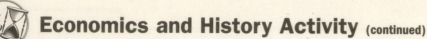

Economics and History Activity (continued)

✓ Applying Economics to History

Directions: Answer the following questions in the spaces provided.

1. **Making Inferences** Why do you think many colonists believed in equality and rights as expressed in the Declaration of Independence yet still engaged in slavery?

_____

_____

_____

2. **Analyzing Visuals** Based on the graphs, what was the trend in the importation of enslaved Africans between 1771 and 1860?

_____

_____

3. **Analyzing Visuals** What was the trend in cotton exportation between 1792 and 1820?

_____

_____

4. **Determining Cause and Effect** What effect did Congress's actions in 1808 have on the importation of enslaved Africans?

_____

_____

5. **Drawing Conclusions** What conclusions can you make about slavery and the southern economy?

_____

_____

GOING FURTHER ▶ ▶▶▶

- Conduct research to learn about the invention of the cotton gin and the effects it had on cotton production and slavery in the United States. Then write a paragraph explaining how these effects are reflected in the graphs on the previous page.

Unit

Reading Skills Activity

The Americas: Worlds Meet

Identifying the Main Idea

✓ Learning the Skill

The question "What is this writing about?" is answered by finding the main idea. Main ideas are the most important ideas in a paragraph, section, or chapter. Supporting details are facts or examples that explain the main idea. Historical details, such as names, dates, and events, are easier to remember when they are connected to a main idea. Understanding the main idea allows you to grasp the whole picture or story.

Use the following guidelines to help you identify the main idea:

- Read the selection carefully and ask, "Why was this written? What is its purpose?"

- Look for the main idea and jot it down in your own words. The main idea is in a topic sentence, which can be found at the beginning, in the middle, or at the end of the paragraph. The main idea of a large section of text is often found in a topic paragraph.

- Reread the selection to see whether other sentences and details support the main idea. Some supporting details are essential in clarifying the main idea, whereas other details are not. When creating a summary graphic organizer, only capture the essential supporting details.

✓ Practicing the Skill

Directions: Read the following passage that describes colonial trade, and then complete the activity on the next page. Two supporting details have been provided to get you started.

Colonial Trade

As the center of the shipping trade in America, New England linked the different English American colonies and linked America to other parts of the world. Some ships followed routes that came to be called the triangular trade because the routes formed a triangle. On one leg of such a route, ships brought sugar and molasses from the West Indies to the New England colonies. In New England, the molasses would be made into rum. Next, the rum and other manufactured goods were shipped to West Africa where they were traded for enslaved Africans. On the final leg of the route, the enslaved Africans were taken to the West Indies where they were sold to planters. The profit was used to buy more molasses, and the process started over.

Reading Skills Activity (continued)

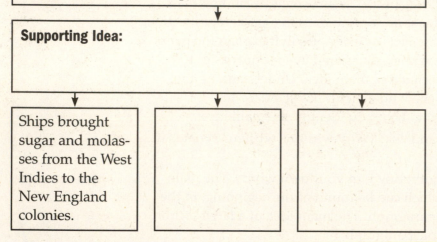

Main Idea:

↓

Supporting Idea:
New England linked the English American colonies to one another and to different parts of the world.

↓

Supporting Idea:

↓   ↓   ↓

Ships brought sugar and molasses from the West Indies to the New England colonies.

✔ Applying the Skill

Directions: Read the passage below, and then on a separate sheet of paper create and fill in a graphic organizer with the main idea and supporting details.

> From the 1720s through the 1740s, an important religious movement called the Great Awakening swept through the colonies. In New England and the Middle Colonies, ministers called for "a new birth," a return to the strong faith of earlier days. Revivalists such as Jonathan Edwards of Massachusetts stressed the importance of personal religious experience. People thought his sermons were powerful and convincing.
>
> English revivalist George Whitefield arrived in the colonies in 1739. A commanding, charismatic speaker, Whitefield's sermons attracted large crowds from New England to Georgia. Whitefield inspired worshipers in churches and revival meetings throughout the colonies.
>
> The Great Awakening increased church membership and strengthened the faith of many colonists. However, conservative, traditional ministers condemned the revivalists (called "New Lights") for their emotional preaching style. In response, many New Lights left the established churches and founded their own. By challenging traditional authority, the Great Awakening helped affirm ideals of independent thought and religious freedom.
>
> Source: TAJ text and James A. Henretta et al, *America's History, Volume 1: To 1877*
> (Boston: Bedford/St. Martin's), pp. 114–115.

Unit

American Literature Reading

The Americas: Worlds Meet

Colonial Poetry

About the Selection

Phillis Wheatley, an African who was enslaved and brought to the American colonies when she was eight years old, arrived in Boston on the schooner *Phillis* on July 11, 1761. Susanna Wheatley of Boston purchased her to help with household tasks. Susanna Wheatley's daughter, Mary, taught Phillis to read and write in English and guided her Christian education. Her slaveholder encouraged Phillis to write and helped her publish her work, an extraordinary accomplishment for an enslaved young female. She wrote the poem, "On Virtue," at about the age of thirteen.

Reader's Dictionary

fathom: to understand

converse: to talk with someone

auspicious: successful, prosperous

pinions: wings

chastity: being pure

retinue: those who accompany a high-ranking person

orbs: heavenly bodies

appellation: name or title

cherubs: child angels

Guided Reading

As you read the poem, try to identify the religious and moral beliefs of Phillis Wheatley.

On Virtue

by Phillis Wheatley, 1766

O Thou bright jewel in my aim I strike
To comprehend thee. Thine own words declare
Wisdom is higher than a fool can reach.
I cease to wonder, and no more attempt
Thine height t'explore, or **fathom** thy profound.
But, O my soul, sink not into despair,
Virtue is near thee, and with gentle hand
Would now embrace thee, hovers o'er thine head.
Fain would the heav'n-born soul with her **converse,**
Then seek, then court her for her promis'd bliss.

Auspicious queen, thine heav'nly **pinions** spread,
And lead celestial **Chastity** along;
Lo! now her sacred **retinue** descends,
Array'd in glory from the **orbs** above.

American Literature Reading (continued)

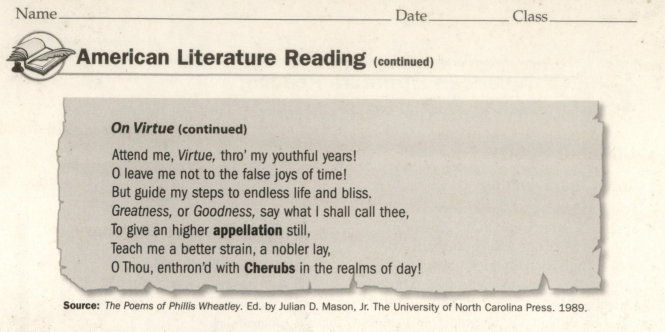

> **On Virtue** (continued)
>
> Attend me, *Virtue*, thro' my youthful years!
> O leave me not to the false joys of time!
> But guide my steps to endless life and bliss.
> *Greatness*, or *Goodness*, say what I shall call thee,
> To give an higher **appellation** still,
> Teach me a better strain, a nobler lay,
> O Thou, enthron'd with **Cherubs** in the realms of day!

Source: *The Poems of Phillis Wheatley.* Ed. by Julian D. Mason, Jr. The University of North Carolina Press. 1989.

Literary Response and Analysis

Directions: Answer the following questions on a separate sheet of paper.

1. **Identifying** Who was the auspicious queen?

2. **Explaining** Why did Wheatley believe she could not completely understand Virtue?

3. **Making Inferences** Why did Wheatley believe there was no need to despair?

4. **Drawing Conclusions** What did Phillis Wheatley believe Virtue would do for her? Use examples from the text in your answer.

Unit

Enrichment Activity

The Americas: Worlds Meet

Human Migration

No one knows exactly when the first people came to America, where they came from, or how they arrived. For decades, most experts thought that the first Americans were the Clovis people, named after a site in Clovis, New Mexico, where stone spear points and other artifacts were found. Using carbon dating, scientists were able to determine that the people who made these artifacts lived in North America about 11,500 years ago. Since the 1970s, however, older sites have been discovered in North and South America. These sites, as well as genetic research, suggest that people may have migrated to the Americas even earlier than was originally believed.

Human Migration Theories

Archaeological Evidence

The first evidence of settlement in the Americas that predates the Clovis people was found at Monte Verde, a site in southern Chile. Scientists have dated the artifacts and remains found at this site to 12,500 years ago. Artifacts found at other sites also seem to suggest that people were in North America even earlier than this. In South Carolina a settlement was found that dates as far back as 18,000 years. The map shows some of the most important archaeological sites in North America.

North America

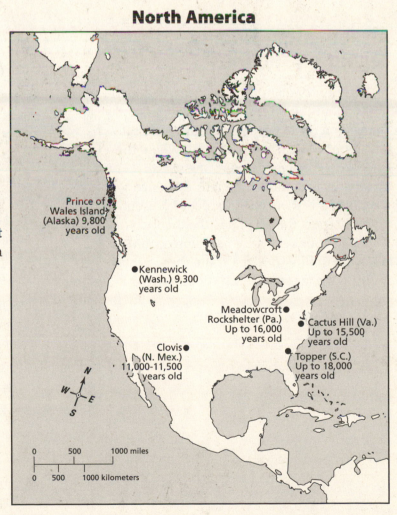

Enrichment Activity (continued)

Genetic Evidence

Another way that scientists are learning about early human migration is through the study of genetics. Occasionally, a person's DNA will mutate, or change. These mutations, called genetic markers, can be passed on from one generation to another. Scientists know that different populations of people, or haplogroups, have their own genetic markers. Scientists use genetic markers and knowledge of haplogroups to trace a person's ancestors back through time to create a genetic family tree. This family tree can help scientists determine how a person's ancestors traveled around the world. These genetic studies have shown that all people share common ancestors in Africa.

To learn how ancient people moved from Africa to other continents around the world, scientists are collecting DNA samples from the world's present-day population. By comparing the DNA of Native Americans to the DNA of people in Asia and Europe, scientists are developing new theories about when people first came to the Americas and where they came from.

Investigating Human Migration Theories

Use library or Internet resources to learn more about the migration of ancient people to the Americas. Focus on a particular theory about how, when, and from where the first people arrived. Determine what archaeological and/or genetic evidence supports this theory. Prepare and present an oral report that explains the theory. Enhance your report by using presentation software to illustrate the route these people might have taken to reach the Americas.

Self-Assessment Checklist

Assess your presentation using the checklist below:

- [ ] My presentation was well organized, with an effective introduction, body, and conclusion.
- [ ] I clearly explained the migration theory and the evidence supporting the theory.
- [ ] I used presentation software effectively to enhance the report.
- [ ] I included a map that showed the route suggested by the migration theory.
- [ ] I spoke clearly and slowly, and made eye contact with the audience.

Interpreting Political Cartoons

The Americas: Worlds Meet

Franklin's Albany Plan of Union and the First Political Cartoon

Benjamin Franklin drew the cartoon below, and it is believed to be the first cartoon published in the United States. He published it in his *Pennsylvania Gazette* on May 9, 1754, just before delegates of the colonists met at the Albany Congress. Franklin hoped it would generate support for his Plan of Union. Franklin's cartoon was later used on flags and posters to support collaborations against British taxation of the colonies under the Stamp Act (1765) and to support revolution (1776).

Directions: Study the cartoon below, and then answer the questions that follow.

Library of Congress, Prints and Photographic Division, LC-USZC4-5315

Interpreting Political Cartoons Activity (continued)

1. Notice the letters next to each piece of the snake. What do these letters stand for?

_____

2. Why does the snake have 8 pieces and not 13?

_____

3. Which of the following slogans best reflects the general theme of Franklin's cartoon? Circle your response.

   A. In unity there is strength.

   B. The whole is greater than the sum of its parts.

   C. Too many cooks spoil the broth.

4. What message was Franklin's cartoon delivering to the delegates at the Albany Congress?

_____

_____

Critical Thinking

5. **Drawing Conclusions** Is Franklin's message still relevant for political life today? Support your answer with specific references.

_____

_____

6. **Analyzing Information** When Franklin drew this cartoon, many people mistakenly believed that if a snake were cut into pieces, the pieces could weave themselves back together. Knowing that this is incorrect, write a new caption for the cartoon to replace "Join, or Die." Explain the meaning of your new caption.

_____

_____

_____

7. **Synthesizing Information** If Franklin were alive today, what symbols could he use to send the same message of unity to Americans? Make a list of possible symbols.

_____

_____

The First Americans

Chapter

Content Vocabulary Activity
The First Americans

Fill in the Blanks DIRECTIONS: Select a term from the box below to complete each of the sentences that follow.

archaeology	maize	theocracy	terrace
artifact	carbon dating	hieroglyphics	pueblo
nomad	culture	Quechua	clan
migration	civilization	quipus	federation

1. Scientists can measure the amount of radioactive carbon in an artifact made from any substance that was once alive using _____.

2. A(n) _____ is a person who moves from place to place.

3. A(n) _____ is a society governed by religious leaders.

4. Modern scientists use _____, the study of ancient peoples, to determine how the first people came to the Americas.

5. The Iroquois people were organized into groups of related families each called a(n) _____.

6. The official language for the Inca Empire was _____.

7. A(n) _____ is a tool, weapon, basket, or carving of early peoples.

8. A(n) _____ is a structure of stone and sundried earth built by the Anasazi people.

9. _____ use symbols or pictures to represent things, ideas, and sounds.

10. Movement of a large number of people into a new land is a(n) _____.

11. Highly developed societies called _____ built enormous cities in thick jungles and on mountaintops that were hard to reach.

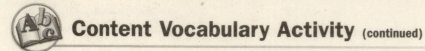

Content Vocabulary Activity (continued)

12. The _____ are various lengths and colors of string used by the Incas to record information.

13. Early Americans learned to plant and raise an early form of corn called

_____ , which, along with other food sources, allowed them to stay in one place.

14. A(n) _____ is a government that links different groups.

15. The Inca cut a broad platform called a(n) _____ into steep slopes in order to plant crops on mountainous lands.

16. A(n) _____ is a person's or group's way of life.

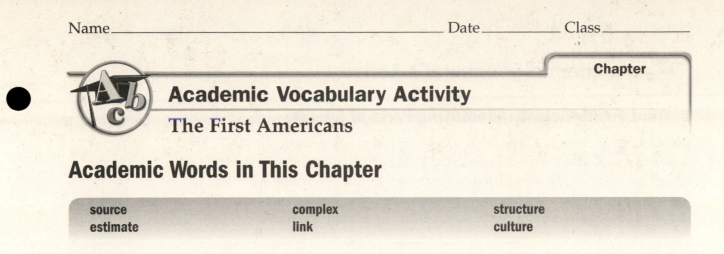

Academic Vocabulary Activity

The First Americans

Academic Words in This Chapter

source	complex	structure
estimate	link	culture

A. Word Meaning Activity: Identifying Synonyms

Directions: Read the underlined words below, as well as the four words or phrases next to them. Circle the word or phrase that is *most similar* in meaning to the underlined word as it is used in the chapter.

1. <u>source:</u>   hunt, lifestyle, water, point of origin

2. <u>estimate:</u>   difference, measurement, value, time

3. <u>complex:</u>   sophisticated, obvious, simple, motivated

4. <u>link:</u>   separate, travel, connect, transport

5. <u>structure:</u>   waterway, building, path, landscape

6. <u>culture:</u>   music, federation, civilization, elegance

B. Word Usage Activity: Using Academic Words

Directions: Use a form of the academic words at the top of this page to replace the underlined common words in the lines below.

1. The Incas <u>integrated</u> their growing population by building thousands of

   miles of roads. _____

2. The large <u>shelters</u> were made of stone and earth. _____

3. Scientists provided <u>approximations</u> of the artwork's possible age.

   _____

4. Early civilizations developed <u>elaborate</u> systems of communication.

   _____

5. The <u>groups of people</u> in Mexico and Central America influenced

   the people living to the north and west. _____

6. Changes in their environment forced early Americans to find other

   <u>possibilities</u> for food. _____

Academic Vocabulary Activity (continued)

C. Word Family Activity: Identifying Parts of Speech

Directions: A *noun* is a word that names a person, place, thing, or idea. A *verb* is a word that is used to describe an action, experience, or state of being. An *adjective* is a word used to describe a noun. Determine whether the words below are in noun, verb, or adjective form. Put a check mark (√) in the appropriate column. Some words have more than one form.

Words	Noun	Verb	Adjective
1. complicate			
2. complex			
3. linked			
4. link			
5. structured			
6. structural			
7. structure			
8. estimation			
9. estimated			
10. estimate			
11. culture			
12. cultural			
13. cultured			

Chapter

Primary Source Readings

The First Americans

Native American Prophecies

Interpreting the Source

Prophecies are said to offer clues and warnings about future events. As you read the Mayan chant and the Aztec song, imagine the images described in each to see how they might appear to be prophecies for the Native Americans.

Guided Reading

As you read the chart and song, think about what these words are predicting.

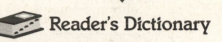

Reader's Dictionary

blight: plant diseases marked by the withering and death of parts like leaves and tubers

marvel: to become filled with surprise, wonder, or amazed curiosity

adobe: a brick or building material made of sun-dried clay and straw

---

Mayan Chant

Eat, eat, while there is bread,
Drink, drink, while there is water;
A day comes when dust shall darken the air,
When a **blight** shall wither the land,
When a cloud shall arise,
When a mountain shall be lifted up,
When a strong man shall seize the city,
When ruin shall fall upon all things,
When the tender leaf shall be destroyed,
When eyes shall be closed in death;
When there shall be three signs on a tree,
Father, son and grandson hanging dead on
  the same tree;
When the battle flag shall be raised,
And the people scattered abroad in the forests.

Source: Daniel G. Brinton. *Essays of an Americanist.* Philadelphia: Porter and Coats, 1890.

Primary Source Readings (continued)

Aztec Song

And all this happened to us.
We saw it,
we **marveled** at it.
With this sad and mournful destiny [future]
We saw ourselves afflicted [suffering].
On the roads lie broken arrows,
our hair in disarray [disorder].
Without roofs are the houses, . . .
We have struggled against the walls of **adobe,**
but our heritage was a net made of holes.
Our shields were our protection
but not even with shields could we defend ourselves. . . .

Source: *MSS Anónimo de Tlatelolco,* in *Historia Tolteca-Chichimeca,* Vol. I of *Corpus Codicum Americanorum Medii Aevi.* Ed. Ernst Mengin. Copenhagen: Sumptibus Einar Munksgaard, 1942, fol. 33.

DBQ Document-Based Questions

Directions: Answer the questions below in the spaces provided.

1. **Analyzing** What event or events did the Maya chant and Aztec song predict?

_____

_____

2. **Identifying** List five words from each passage that give the reader a sense of doom.

_____

_____

3. **Evaluating** Choose an image from one of the passages and describe how it makes you feel.

_____

_____

4. **Making Inferences** What is the general message of the chant and song?

_____

_____

5. **Making Connections** Identify other prophecies in history that have offered clues and warnings.

_____

_____

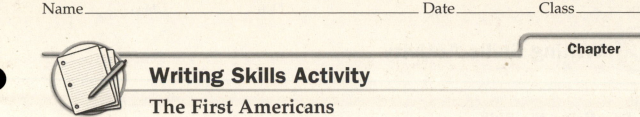

Writing Skills Activity

The First Americans

Writing Topic Sentences and Supporting Details

✓ Learning the Skill

A good paragraph is more than a series of sentences. It is an informational unit in which all the sentences work together to make a point.

When you write, make sure each paragraph focuses on one main idea. State this idea in a **topic sentence** that lets readers know what the paragraph is about. Use other sentences with **supporting details** to build upon the topic sentence. These supporting sentences should relate to the main idea.

The topic sentence tells readers what the paragraph is about.

This supporting sentence expands on the main idea.

This supporting sentence expands on the main idea.

This sentence does not relate to the main idea and should be deleted.

The early cultures of Mexico and Central America appear to have influenced people living in central North America. *Prehistoric Native Americans built thousands of mounds of earth that look very much like the stone pyramids of the Maya and Aztec.* The mounds have been found as far north as the Great Lakes. *Some were topped with temples, as in the Maya and Aztec cultures.*

Types of topic sentences

A topic sentence can:

- announce the topic—*Among the earliest Mound Builders were the Adena.*
- serve as a transition from the previous paragraph—*Like the Adena, the Hopewell people were Mound Builders.*
- ask and answer a question—*What is Cahokia? It was the largest settlement of Mound Builders in what is currently known as Illinois.*

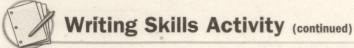

Writing Skills Activity (continued)

✔ Practicing the Skill

Directions: For each set of details below, write one topic sentence.

Topic Sentence (main idea)	Supporting Sentences
1. _____ _____	• One theory stated that the mound builders were Vikings who came to America and then disappeared. • Another theory suggested that people from the lost continent of Atlantis built the mounds.
2. _____ _____	• Warfare between Mississippian societies over farm-land increased. • Europeans introduced new diseases that caused the population to decline in Mississippian societies.
3. _____ _____	• Mounds can be found in the shape of animals, cones, and pyramids. • Native Americans used the mounds as burial places and foundations of buildings.

✔ Applying the Skill

Directions: Write a brief paragraph about one of the topics below. Your paragraph should begin with a topic sentence that focuses on one main idea. This topic sentence should be followed by at least two supporting sentences.

• regions where Native Americans lived
• types of Native American housing
• types of Native American communities

A topic sentence that makes one point about your idea:

_____

_____

Two or more supporting sentences:

_____

_____

_____

_____

Self-Assessment Checklist

Assess your paragraph using the checklist below:

☐ I included one specific point about the topic in the topic sentence.

☐ I supported the topic sentence with at least one detail in each supporting sentence.

☐ I reviewed my paragraph to make sure each sentence relates to the topic sentence.

☐ I eliminated any sentence that does not belong.

Social Studies Skills Activity

The First Americans

Reading a Time Line

✓ Learning the Skill

Historians create time lines to show when key events occurred during a particular historical period. A time line begins with a specific date and ends with another date. All the events between these dates happened in the order in which they are listed, from left to right. Reading time lines is an easy way to make sense of the flow of events and when they occurred. A time line also gives you a picture of history and the relationships among events.

Use the following steps to read a time line:

- Read the title of the time line to understand what time period is being presented.
- Determine the time span, or the beginning and ending dates.
- Determine the time intervals. This is the length of the smaller segments of time used to divide the period on the time line.
- Identify the individual events labeled along the time line. Look for relationships among the events.

✓ Practicing the Skill

Directions: Read the information on the time line below, and then answer the questions that follow.

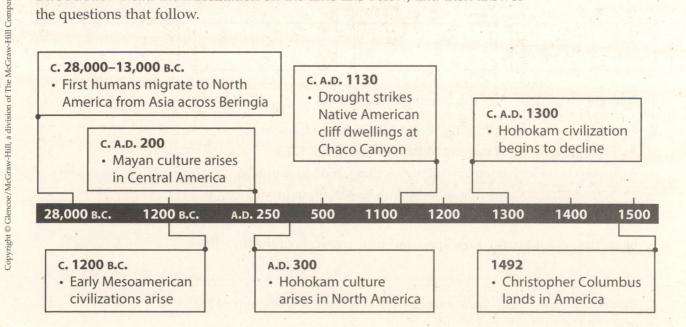

Copyright © Glencoe/McGraw-Hill, a division of The McGraw-Hill Companies, Inc.

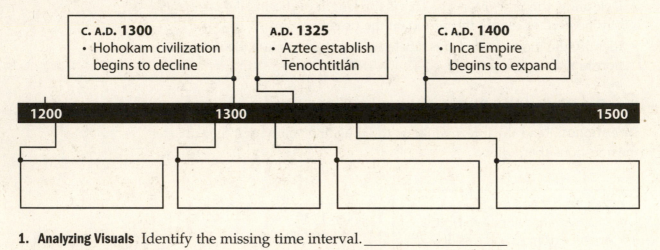

Social Studies Skills Activity (continued)

1. **Finding the main idea** What is the purpose of the time line on the previous page?

_____

2. **Identifying** What is the time span for this time line? What are the intervals

on this time line?_____

3. **Locating** Where did the first human migration to North America occur?

_____

4. **Specifying** When did a drought affect the culture living in Chaco Canyon?

_____

Applying the Skill

Directions: Read the information on the time line below, and then answer the questions that follow.

C. A.D. **1300**	A.D. **1325**	C. A.D. **1400**
• Hohokam civilization begins to decline	• Aztec establish Tenochtitlán	• Inca Empire begins to expand

1200   **1300**   **1500**

1. **Analyzing Visuals** Identify the missing time interval._____

2. **Sequencing** Add the following world events to the time line:
   - England's King John signs Magna Carta in A.D. 1215.
   - Italian traveler Marco Polo returns from China in A.D. 1295.
   - Mansa Musa begins rule of West African Kingdom of Mali in A.D. 1312.
   - In A.D. 1368, Ming dynasty begins in China.

3. **Identifying** What are the time span and time intervals of the time line?

_____

4. **Calculating** How much time passed between the establishment of Mali and the founding of Tenochtitlán?

_____

Differentiated Instruction Activity

The First Americans

The Achievements of the Inca

The ancient Inca had neither the wheel nor a written language. Nevertheless, their inventions and engineering achievements were spectacular.

Perhaps the Inca's greatest accomplishment was a tool called a quipu, which they used to keep records and create messages. A quipu consisted of a long main string to which were tied many additional colored strings. Each string was knotted. The string color and the distance between the knots had meaning to the Inca. A yellow string, for instance, might have represented maize or gold.

An extensive system of stone roads—encompassing perhaps as many as 30,000 miles (48.28 km)—helped facilitate communication and the transfer of goods throughout the Inca Empire. Two main north-south roads were joined by smaller crossroads. All of the roads were built using the natural resources and geography of the region. The Inca also built suspension bridges of fiber ropes to cross the deep river gorges. Some of these bridges were more than 150 feet long.

The mountainous environment of the Andes made agriculture difficult for the Inca, so they used a method of terrace farming. They cut raised, level ledges in a step pattern along the sides of hills to create more usable cropland. Terrace farming also prevented topsoil from washing away.

The Inca were great builders. They were skilled stonecutters whose masonry required no mortar. The great stones used for buildings at sites such as Machu Picchu weighed many tons, yet they were so expertly carved and fitted together that it is still impossible to slip a knife blade between them.

Other Inca achievements include freeze-dried foods, beautiful textiles and metalwork, a complex series of irrigation canals and aqueducts, and a wide array of musical instruments. The Spanish conquistadors who arrived in the early 1500s were astounded by their accomplishments.

Directions: Use the information from the excerpt and your textbook to answer the following questions on a separate sheet of paper.

1. **Comparing** Identify some tools or objects mentioned in the passage that were used by *both* the ancient Inca and modern Americans.

2. **Evaluating** Which of the achievements or inventions discussed in the passage do you think did the most to preserve the history of the Inca? To assist the spread of the Inca Empire? To feed the Inca? Explain your answers.

Differentiated Instruction Activity (continued)

Teaching Strategies for Different Learning Styles

The following activities are ways the basic lesson can be modified to accommodate students' different learning styles.

English Language Learner (ELL)

Ask students to select four inventions or achievements mentioned in the passage and write a sentence or two about what they are and how they are used.

Gifted and Talented

Ask students to prepare an essay about the use and purpose of the Inca road system. Also have them speculate on how the advanced Inca road system might have worked against them when the Spanish conquistadors arrived.

Verbal/Linguistic; Interpersonal

Briefly recount for students the rediscovery of the lost Inca city of Machu Picchu in 1911 and how Peru has recently demanded the return from Yale University of the artifacts taken from there. Assign students to one of two groups—one favoring the relics' return, the other opposing it—for participation in a class debate. Students should thoroughly research both sides of the issue. Stress to students that they do not need to personally believe the position they will argue, but they do need to argue convincingly and provide ample evidence for their views. Allow each student an opportunity to speak in class.

Logical/Mathematical

Archaeologists believe that most information on a quipu is numeric—numbers being represented as a sequence of knot clusters using base 10. Ask students to research this topic, work out a system for representing numbers on a quipu, and then create their own. Have students demonstrate to their classmates how their quipus are read.

Visual/Spatial; Intrapersonal

Ask students to use library and Internet resources to construct a map of the Inca road system. Students' maps should clearly identify major roads (e.g., Camino Real, El Camino de la Costa) as well as major cities and archaeological sites (e.g., Chavin, Tiwanaku, Machu Picchu, Cuzco).

Kinesthetic

Scholars are not sure how the Inca moved the huge stones they used for construction without wheeled vehicles, pulleys, or animal-drawn carts. Ask students to research the topic, and then prepare an in-class demonstration to show one possible way the Inca might have done this (e.g., by using sliders).

Naturalist

Ask students to use library and Internet resources to provide examples of how the Inca used and adapted the natural materials they found in their environment (e.g., bridges made from grass fibers).

Below Grade Level

A K-W-L chart taps student knowledge and generates interest. Have students create a three-column chart titled *Inca Achievements*. Explain that they will fill out the chart by writing what they **K**now about the topic in the first column, what they **W**ant to know in the second, and what they **L**earned in the third. Have students first fill out the **K** and **W** columns. Then ask them to complete the **L** column as they study the passage and/or conduct their own library or Internet research.

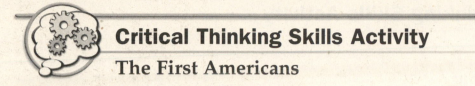

Critical Thinking Skills Activity

The First Americans

Analyzing Visual Information

✓ Learning the Skill

Population density maps use colors or symbols to show the average number of people living in a square mile or square kilometer. An area with a high population density has more people per square mile or kilometer than an area with low population density. When you analyze visual information, you look for titles to describe the visual. Looking for keys and labels in maps helps you determine what the map is about.

Native American Population Density in North America, 1500

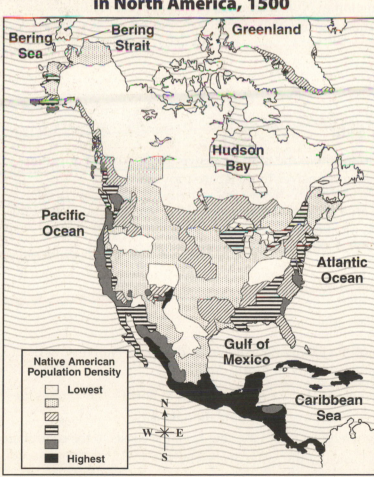

Native American Population Density

☐ Lowest

▨

⊘

☰

▨

■ Highest

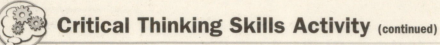

Critical Thinking Skills Activity (continued)

✓ Practicing the Skill

Directions: Use the map on the previous page to answer the questions below.

1. Interpreting Describe the purpose of the map.

_____

_____

2. Analyzing Which area of North America had the highest Native American population density in 1500?

_____

_____

3. Analyzing Which region in North America had the lowest Native American population density in 1500?

_____

_____

✓ Applying the Skill

Directions: Use information in the map to answer the following questions. Put the letter of the correct answer in the space provided.

_____ 1. Which area symbol appears where the Native American population is most dense?

    A. a white area

    B. a dotted area

    C. a striped area

    D. a black area

_____ 2. Which of the following statements describes Native American population density in North America?

    A. It generally decreases from south to north.

    B. All islands have low population density.

    C. It generally increases moving from the coasts to the central areas.

    D. It is basically the same everywhere.

Geography and History Activity

The First Americans

Early Native American Cultures

Early North Americans developed ways of life that were well adapted to their environments. The Anasazi in the Southwest built cliff dwellings for protection and shelter in areas such as Arizona and New Mexico.

Native Americans who settled in the Far North regions near the Arctic Ocean are called Inuit. They built igloos and wore furs and sealskins, which were warm and waterproof. They hunted and fished for their food.

The Tlingit, Haida, and Chinook settled along the West Coast with its mild climate and reliable food sources from the forest and the sea. They built wooden houses and made canoes from tree bark. Salmon was the main food of people in the Northwest.

In California's desert areas, nomadic groups like the Pomo wandered from place to place, gathering roots and seeds. In the arid Great Basin between the Sierra Nevada and the Rocky Mountains, the soil was too hard and rocky for farming. There the Shoshone traveled for food and made temporary shelters from branches and reeds.

The Hopi, the Acoma, and the Zuni peoples were Southwestern descendants of the Anasazi. They constructed their homes from adobe, bricks made of dried dirt and straw. Corn and maize served as their basic foods. The Apache and the Navajo settled in this region in the 1500s. They were hunters and gatherers, lived in square houses called *hogans*, and grew maize and beans.

The Great Plains was home to other nomadic peoples. When they moved their villages from place to place, they dragged their tepees behind them. The men hunted buffalo and deer, and the women raised maize, squash, and beans.

The Comanche, the Dakota, and other Plains peoples captured and tamed wild horses. They became skilled riders and used their horses for hunting and warfare.

In the woodlands of eastern North America, the Iroquois and Cherokee created laws and formed governments. The Iroquois were mainly farmers, raising crops like corn, squash, and tobacco. They lived in communal longhouses that were covered in bark. The woodlands of the Southeast, inhabited by the Creek, Chickasaw, and Cherokee, were warmer than the eastern woodlands. The Chickasaw lived in the area that is now Mississippi, and farmed the river bottomlands. They constructed dwellings made of pole frames, with thatch, hide, mud, or bark coverings.

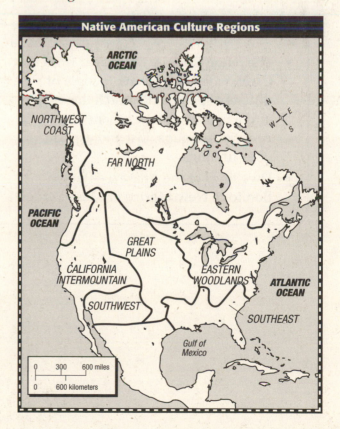

Native American Culture Regions

Geography and History Activity (continued)

✓ Applying Geography to History

Directions: Answer the questions below using the map and the spaces provided.

1. **Identifying** Using different colored crayons or pencils, shade in each Native American culture region on the map.

2. **Illustrating** Important foods in some of the Native American culture regions included fish, corn, acorns, or buffalo meat. Draw a picture of a food that was grown or hunted in each region on the map.

3. **Making Connections** Select one of the types of dwellings used by early Native Americans. Explain why it was suitable for that region of North America.

_____

_____

4. **Locating** Write the number of each of the following characteristics on the appropriate region of the map. (1) rode horses in warfare; (2) created a government; (3) clothing made from fur and sealskins; (4) used resources of the forest and sea; (5) nomadic; (6) Apache and Navajo; (7) farmed river bottomlands.

5. **Drawing Conclusions** What conclusions can you draw about early Native Americans from the information in the article and on the map?

_____

_____

GOING FURTHER ▶ ▶▶▶

- The name *Cherokee* originated from a Creek word that means "people of different speech." Research the origin of the names of three other Native American groups. List and explain your findings.
- Dwellings of the Anasazi—Pueblo Bonito in New Mexico or Mesa Verde in Colorado—can still be seen in the Southwest today. Conduct research into one of the Anasazi stone dwellings or cliff dwellings in the Southwest. Write a brief report describing in detail what the dwelling was like during the time of the Anasazi.

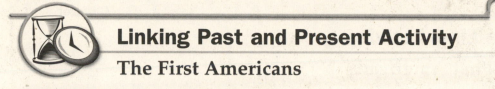

Chapter

Linking Past and Present Activity

The First Americans

Agriculture in the Americas

THEN **Corn** Native Americans cultivated corn as early as 3500 B.C. Early farmers often sowed several fields in the hopes that one would flourish. They frequently grew crops in dried-up riverbeds, where roots could reach water.

Thousands of years before there were movie theaters, Native Americans ate popcorn. They also ground corn into meal, which they stored throughout the winter and baked into cakes.

Maple Syrup Long before Europeans came to the Americas, Native Americans of the Northeast Woodlands made sugar and syrup from the sap of sugar maples. They tapped holes into the trees, collected the sap, and then boiled it down or let it evaporate. Eight pounds (3.6 kg) of sap produced one pound (.45 kg) of sugar.

NOW **Corn** Today corn is one of the most important crops in the United States. Americans eat corn cooked, on and off the cob; they make it into corn bread, tortillas, and cereal. Corn syrup, corn oil, and cornstarch are common ingredients in processed foods. Corn is also an important food for livestock.

Corn has also become an important energy source. Corn is used to produce ethanol, which can be mixed with gasoline to produce fuels that most vehicles can use. In 2007 the United States grew more than 13 billion bushels of corn.

Maple Syrup Today maple syrup is still produced mainly in North America. The tapping process is now mechanized, and plastic tubing transports sap to large evaporation plants. It takes about 30 to 50 gallons (114 to 189 L) of sap to make one gallon (3.8 L) of syrup.

Directions: Answer the questions below on a separate sheet of paper.

1. **Describing** What techniques did Native Americans develop for raising corn?

2. **Explaining** How did Native Americans produce sugar from sap?

3. **Drawing Conclusions** Why could corn be called a multipurpose crop?

4. **Contrasting** How does the way in which early Native Americans made maple syrup differ from the way in which it is made today?

5. **Hypothesizing** How do you think the discovery of maple syrup came about?

Time Line Activity

The First Americans

Cultures of the Americas Before 1492

Directions: Use your textbook and the information below to complete the time line. Place events in the appropriate spaces. Include the date for each event.

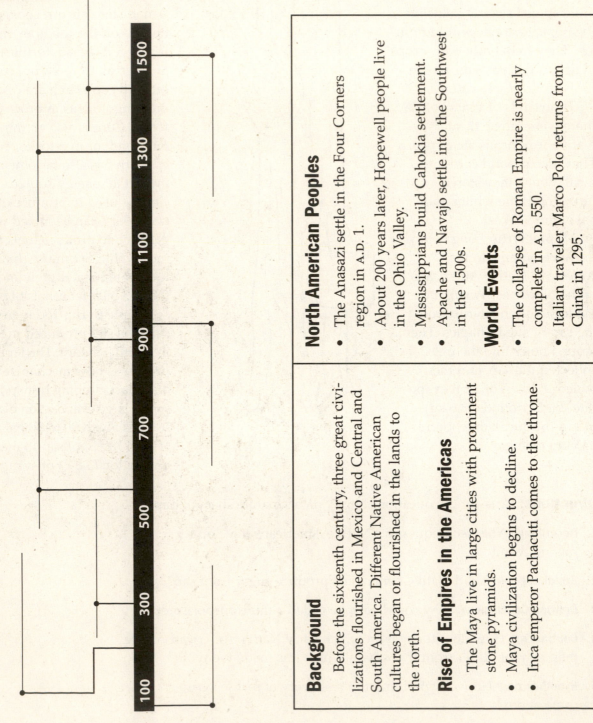

North American Peoples

- The Anasazi settle in the Four Corners region in A.D. 1.
- About 200 years later, Hopewell people live in the Ohio Valley.
- Mississippians build Cahokia settlement.
- Apache and Navajo settle into the Southwest in the 1500s.

World Events

- The collapse of Roman Empire is nearly complete in A.D. 550.
- Italian traveler Marco Polo returns from China in 1295.

Background

Before the sixteenth century, three great civilizations flourished in Mexico and Central and South America. Different Native American cultures began or flourished in the lands to the north.

Rise of Empires in the Americas

- The Maya live in large cities with prominent stone pyramids.
- Maya civilization begins to decline.
- Inca emperor Pachacuti comes to the throne.

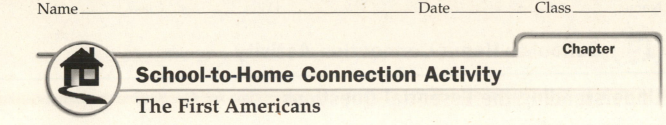

Chapter

School-to-Home Connection Activity

The First Americans

What Do You Know?

Directions: Ask each other the following questions to see how much you know about the first Americans.*

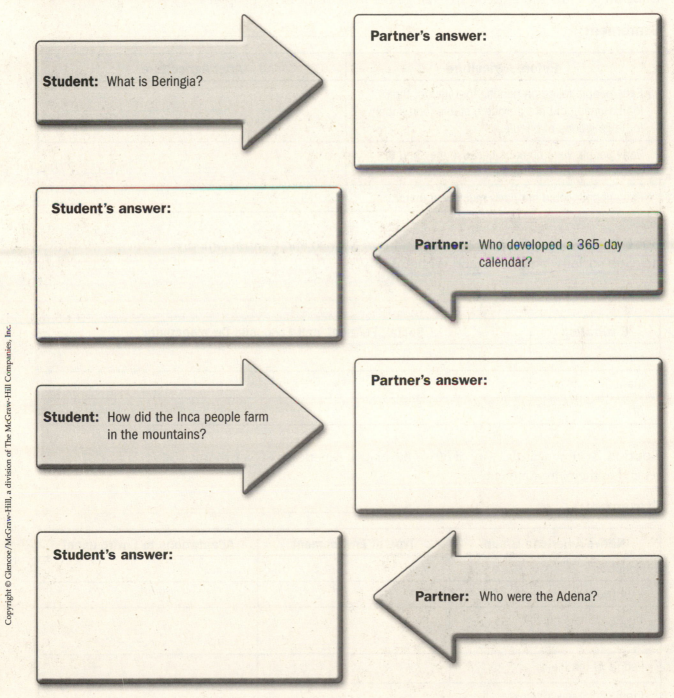

Student: What is Beringia?

Partner's answer:

Student's answer:

Partner: Who developed a 365 day calendar?

Student: How did the Inca people farm in the mountains?

Partner's answer:

Student's answer:

Partner: Who were the Adena?

*With your student, find answers to these questions in the student textbook.

🏠 School-to-Home Connection Activity (continued)

Understanding the Essential Questions

Directions: Rewrite each Essential Question as a statement. Then use your textbook to help you write details that support your statement in the graphic organizer provided.

Section 1 How did agriculture change the lives of the early people?

Statement: _____

Before Agriculture	After Agriculture
Early people relied on hunting for much of their food. Hunting did not provide a stable food supply for large groups of people.	
Early people were nomads because they had to follow the herds they hunted.	
Early people could not carry much with them.	

Section 2 How did the early civilizations of Mexico and Central America develop socially, politically, and economically?

Statement: _____

Civilization	Social, Political, and Economic Developments
Olmec	
Maya	
Aztec	

Section 3 How was the way of life of the Native Americans of North America related to their environment?

Statement: _____

Native American Group	Type of Environment	Adaptations to Environment
Hohokam		
Inuit (North)		
Tlingit, Haida, Chinook (Northwest)		
People of the Plains		
Creek, Chicksaw, Cherokee (Southeast)		

Chapter

Reteaching Activity

The First Americans

A variety of resources are found throughout the regions of the Americas. Early Native Americans used the resources available in their region to help them survive. They built homes from materials that were native to their area. They hunted animals and ate foods that were unique to the region in which they lived. Each Native American group developed a way of life that was well adapted to the environment.

Completing a Diagram **DIRECTIONS:** From the list below, identify the environment in which each Native American group lived. Then, find the phrase that explains how each group adapted to that environment. Write the number and letter of each item in the appropriate box.

Environments

1. steep canyons of present-day Colorado
2. mountainous regions of present-day Colombia, Argentina, and Chile
3. grasslands of the Great Plains
4. cold, icy lands near the Arctic Ocean
5. dry, hot desert of present-day Arizona

Adaptations

A. hunted grazing animals such as buffalo
B. cut terraces into slopes to plant crops
C. dug irrigation channels
D. built dwellings in cliff walls
E. built igloos

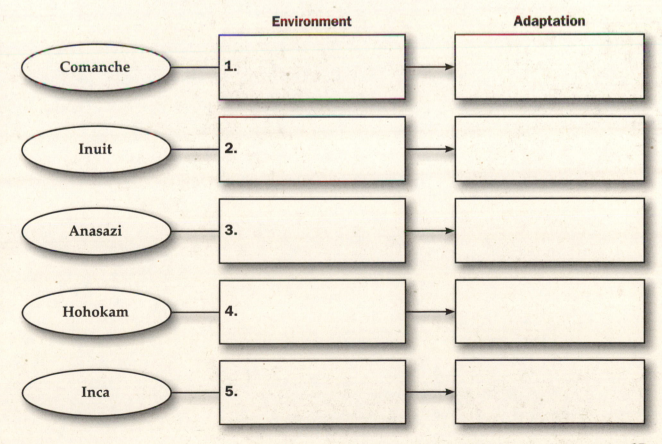

Section Resources

Guided Reading Activity

The First Americans

Migration to the Americas

Reading Tip

As you read the section, write down any words you do not understand. Come back to those words later, look them up in a dictionary, and then try to use them in the context of the chapter.

Answering Questions   DIRECTIONS: Reading the section and completing the questions below will help you learn about the migration to the Americas. Use your textbook to answer the questions.

1. **Defining** What are artifacts?

_____

2. **Explaining** How do archaeologists explain how the first peoples came to the Americas?

_____

3. **Naming** What is the name of the land bridge that once joined Asia and the Americas?

_____

4. **Specifying** When did the most recent Ice Age begin and end?

_____

5. **Identifying** What name is given to people who move from place to place?

_____

6. **Describing** How were mammoths used by the early Americans?

_____

7. **Determining Cause and Effect** Why did the early Americans start to farm?

_____

8. **Analyzing** What effect did farming have on people?

_____

9. **Defining** What is carbon dating?

_____

Section

Guided Reading Activity

The First Americans

Cities and Empires

Reading Tip

After you have read the text under a heading, try to summarize it in one or two sentences.

Outlining   DIRECTIONS: Reading the section and completing the outline below will help you learn more about cities and empires. Refer to your textbook to fill in the blanks.

I. The Olmec, Maya, and Aztec

   A. The Olmec flourished between _____ and

   _____ .

   B. The Maya built large cities, each containing at least one stone

   pyramid with a _____ on top.

     1. The Maya civilization was a(n) _____ , ruled by religious leaders.

     2. The Maya developed a form of writing called _____ .

     3. Maya traders traveled on roads carved out of the _____

     and by canoes up and down _____ east coast.

   C. The Aztec were located in central _____

     1. The capital of _____ was once the largest city in the Americas.

     2. The civilization grew into a(n) _____ empire, conquering rival communities.

     3. The Aztec believed _____ were necessary to please the gods.

II. The Inca

   A. The Inca Empire was the _____ of the early American civilizations.

   B. The Inca state was built on _____ .

   C. The official language of the Inca Empire was _____ .

Section

Guided Reading Activity

The First Americans

North American Peoples

Reading Tip   You will understand what you read better if you form a question out of the text heading. Then read the text below the heading to find the answer to your question.

Reading for Accuracy   DIRECTIONS: Use your textbook to decide if a statement is true or false. Write **T** or **F** in the blank. If a statement is false, rewrite it to make it true.

_____ 1. The Hohokam depended on irrigation channels they dug to carry river water to their fields.

_____

_____ 2. The Hohokam lived in pueblos and cliff dwellings.

_____

_____ 3. Among the earliest Mound Builders were the Cahokia, who were hunters and gatherers.

_____

_____ 4. The people who settled in the lands around the Arctic Ocean are called the Inuit.

_____

_____ 5. Salmon was important to the Tlingit, Ute, and Shoshone.

_____

_____ 6. The Apache and the Navaho in the Southwest built adobe homes and raised corn as their basic food.

_____

_____ 7. The people of the Great Plains lived in tepees.

_____

_____ 8. Members of the Iroquois League were organized by the amount of wealth they had.

_____

_____ 9. Native Americans of the Southeast included the Creek, Chickasaw, and Cherokee.

_____

Exploring the Americas

Content Vocabulary Activity

Exploring the Americas

Defining **DIRECTIONS:** Select a term that matches each definition below. Write the correct term in the space provided.

classical	saga	mission
technology	line of demarcation	encomienda
astrolabe	strait	plantation
pilgrimage	circumnavigate	mercantilism
mosque	conquistador	Northwest Passage
Quran	pueblo	Columbian Exchange
coureur de bois		

1. *Definition:* the holy book of Islam

   Term: _____

2. *Definition:* a traditional story, often focusing on travels or adventures

   Term: _____

3. *Definition:* exchange of goods and ideas between the continents of Europe, Asia, Africa, and the Americas

   Term: _____

4. *Definition:* Spanish explorers who received grants from the rulers of Spain

   Term: _____

5. *Definition:* Muslim place of worship

   Term: _____

6. *Definition:* an imaginary boundary between the land owned by either Spain or Portugal

   Term: _____

7. *Definition:* the economic theory that holds a nation's power is based on its wealth

   Term: _____

📖 Content Vocabulary Activity (continued)

8. *Definition:* ancient Greek and Roman works

Term: _____

9. *Definition:* an instrument used by sailors that measures the position of stars

Term: _____

10. *Definition:* a term used to describe French trappers

Term: _____

11. *Definition:* Spanish towns that were established as centers of trade

Term: _____

12. *Definition:* a narrow sea passage

Term: _____

13. *Definition:* a journey to a holy place

Term: _____

14. *Definition:* the right, granted to conquistadors, to demand taxes or labor from Native Americans living on the land

Term: _____

15. *Definition:* a sought-after direct water route to Asia through the Americas

Term: _____

16. *Definition:* a large estate developed by the Spanish to raise tobacco and sugarcane

Term: _____

17. *Definition:* the use of scientific knowledge for practical purposes

Term: _____

18. *Definition:* to sail around a large area, such as the world

Term: _____

19. *Definition:* religious communities that include a small town, surrounding farmland, and a church

Term: _____

Academic Vocabulary Activity

Exploring the Americas

Academic Words in This Chapter

acquire	devote	grant	globe
impose	alter	found	chart

A. Word Meaning Activity: Matching Words to Definitions

Directions: Match the academic words in Column A to their definitions in Column B.

Column A	Column B
_____ **1.** acquire	**A.** special privilege
_____ **2.** impose	**B.** commit time, money, or effort
_____ **3.** devote	**C.** establish
_____ **4.** alter	**D.** obtain or come into possession
_____ **5.** grant	**E.** planet Earth
_____ **6.** found	**F.** change
_____ **7.** globe	**G.** to make a map of or plan for
_____ **8.** chart	**H.** apply or set by force or authority

Chapter

Differentiated Instruction Activity
Exploring the Americas

The Development of Cartography

Cartography is the art and science of making maps. The oldest known maps are preserved on Babylonian clay tablets from about 2300 B.C. Maps also have been found in Mesopotamia dating from around 1600 B.C. These maps generally recorded simple details, but they formed the basis for the maps we use today.

By the time of the ancient Greeks, cartography had made considerable advances. The concept of a spherical Earth was well-known by the time of Aristotle, around 350 B.C. Ancient Greeks' knowledge of the world, however, extended only to the areas just beyond the Mediterranean Sea. The Greek Anaximander is believed to have made the first map to represent the known world sometime in the 600s B.C. By 250 B.C., Greek geographer Eratosthenes created a map showing Europe on the northwest, Asia on the east, and Libya to the south.

Greek cartography reached its peak when mathematician Ptolemy (circa A.D. 85–165) created a world map. The map illustrated the Old World between the latitudes of 60° N and 30° S. Although Ptolemy's maps had many errors, they were the first to use a mathematically accurate form of projection. Ptolemy's *Guide to Geography* remained a reliable reference on world geography until the Renaissance.

For several centuries, European mapmaking all but ceased. European maps of the Middle Ages reflected Christian beliefs rather than scientific principles. For example, they typically depicted the city of Jerusalem at the center of the world. During this same period, however, Arab cartographers made highly accurate maps based on their own observations and travels, as well as principles they learned from Ptolemy. Arabian geographer al-Idrisi prepared a map of the explored world in 1154.

In the 1200s, European mapmakers again began attempting to draw what they observed of Earth's surface. The invention of printing made maps more widely available. By the 1400s, editions of Ptolemy's maps were being printed in Europe. The discovery of new lands by European explorers also inspired a return to scientific, realistic cartography. By the early 1500s, the first modern atlas was published.

Directions: Use the information from the excerpt and your textbook to answer the following questions on a separate sheet of paper.

1. **Sequencing** Create a time line for the history of cartography based on the information in the excerpt.

2. **Contrasting** How were European maps in the Middle Ages different from Arabic maps of the same time period?

Differentiated Instruction Activity (continued)

Teaching Strategies for Different Learning Styles

The following activities are ways the basic lesson can be modified to accommodate students' different learning styles.

English Language Learner (ELL)

Have students list any words in the excerpt that they do not understand. Students should look up the words in a dictionary and record the definitions. Then encourage students to reread the excerpt.

Special Needs

Show students several different types of maps (political maps, street maps, physical maps, and so forth). Prompt them to identify different uses for each.

Gifted and Talented

Ask students to use library and Internet resources to write a continuation of the essay on the development of cartography from Martin Waldseemüller's 1513 atlas to modern times.

Logical/Mathematical

Ask students to research at least 10 famous names associated with mapmaking to create a table similar to the one shown below. Students should select individuals from a variety of eras and countries.

Name	Era/Country	Accomplishment
Strabo	circa 63 B.C.–A.D. 21 Greece	wrote one of the earliest books on geography

Logical/Mathematical

Explain to students that because the Earth is round and paper is flat, it is hard to draw a map without distorting the shape of the earth. Mapmakers decide the type of projection to use based on who will be using the map. Have students find examples of each of these common types of map projections: equivalent (or equal-area), conformal (or Mercator), and azimuthal equidistant. Ask students to provide definitions of each type of map.

Visual/Spatial; Interpersonal

Assign small groups of students to create a map of their neighborhood or community. Students should draw their maps to scale and include a compass rose and map key. Maps should include streets, important buildings (e.g., school, post office), and other notable landmarks. When groups have completed their assignment, have students compare maps while discussing these questions: Which maps seem the most accurate? Which map would be the most useful for a stranger to find his or her way around the neighborhood? What techniques were the most helpful in figuring out how to make the maps? Why were certain things included or excluded?

Kinesthetic; Intrapersonal

Ask students to research any three of the following and suggest how they aided mapmaking: telescope, pendulum clock, compass, bubble level, aneroid barometer, astrolabe, theodolite, sextant, chromolithography, aerial balloon. Encourage students to construct simple versions of some of these instruments to demonstrate their use for the class. (Directions for creating an astrolabe, sextant, theodolite, compass, and telescope can easily be found online.)

Below Grade Level

Have students read the passage and then write six questions about the material, using a different question starter for each: *who, what, when, where, why,* and *how.*

Name_____ Date_____ Class_____

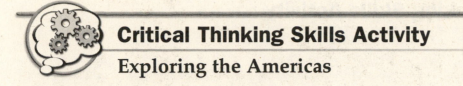

Chapter

Critical Thinking Skills Activity
Exploring the Americas

Determining Cause and Effect

✔ Learning the Skill

When **determining cause and effect,** look for an event (the cause) that makes something else happen (the effect). For example, when European settlers came to the Americas, they unknowingly exposed the Native Americans to diseases. The arrival of the Europeans was the *cause* that resulted in the *effect* of the deaths of many Native Americans.

✔ Practicing the Skill

Directions: Read each passage and write the cause and the effect in the space provided.

1. Wealthy Europeans wanted spices, perfumes, and silks from Asia. Italian merchants bought the Asian goods from Arab traders and then sent the goods to ports on the Mediterranean Sea to ship to Europe.

   Cause   **Effect**

   _____   _____

   _____   _____

2. During the 1400s, mapmakers made land and sea maps that showed ocean currents and lines of latitude and longitude. Better navigation equipment was developed, and there were major advances in ship design. By the mid-1400s, explorers were setting out on longer ocean voyages.

   Cause   **Effect**

   _____   _____

   _____   _____

3. During the 1400s Spain was searching for a way to share in the riches of the Asian trade. In the late 1400s, Queen Isabella financed the expedition of Christopher Columbus, an explorer who hoped to reach Asia by sailing westward across the Atlantic Ocean.

   Cause   **Effect**

   _____   _____

   _____   _____

Critical Thinking Skills Activity (continued)

✓ Applying the Skill

Directions: In the blank at the left, write the letter of the choice that best represents the effect of each of the events.

_____ 1. Christopher Columbus, sailing for Spain, reached the Caribbean as well as Central America and South America.

    A. Spain established a claim on the Caribbean, Central America, and South America.

    B. Spain shared in the riches of the Far East.

    C. Portugal established a claim on Brazil.

    D. Columbus sailed to the Americas with three ships on his first voyage.

_____ 2. The French established early settlements in what is now Quebec, Canada.

    A. Canada became a part of the British Empire.

    B. France founded the city of New Orleans.

    C. French language and culture took root in Quebec.

    D. Ottawa became the capital of Canada.

_____ 3. In the 1400s, Portuguese sailors explored the African coast and rounded the southern tip of the continent to reach the Indian Ocean.

    A. Portugal claimed Brazil as its territory.

    B. The Portuguese established one of the first trade routes to Asia, around Africa's southern tip.

    C. The power of the Portuguese decreased in later centuries.

    D. The Portuguese established extensive sugar plantations in South America.

_____ 4. The voyage to Asia around the southern tip of either Africa or South America was long and dangerous.

    A. Countries such as France, England, and the Netherlands tried to find a more direct route through North America—a Northwest Passage.

    B. Africans were suspicious of some of the seafarers that landed on their coast.

    C. The passages around the southern tip of Africa and South America became popular with sailors of many countries.

    D. The Spanish and Portuguese claimed territory in the Americas.

Chapter

Geography and History Activity

Exploring the Americas

Looking at the Land

European explorers set sail with dreams of glory and discovery in the late 1400s. The vast wilderness of the Americas held the promise of great riches. What form these riches took—gold, furs, or land for settlement—depended on the perception of the adventurer. How did the adventurers' views reflect the goals of the countries for which they sailed?

Goals of the Early Explorers

Spanish explorers searched for landscapes similar to those of their European homeland. Spaniards had learned to mine the mineral ores from Spain's low mountainous terrain. Knowing the economic importance of mineral ores, the earliest Spanish explorers were drawn to the mountainous areas of Mexico and what is today the southwest United States. In these places, mining operations could be established quickly. Explorers were more eager to make quick profits from mining than to develop self-sufficient colonies based on agriculture.

The French, too, were eager to profit from North America's natural resources. The French explored the St. Lawrence River system and the northern Appalachian area and claimed those places for France. Finding a region teeming with beaver, muskrat, and deer, the French turned to trading for furs from animals hunted by Native Americans. The French built a fur-trading monopoly that brought them great wealth.

The English Perception

"There are valleys and plains streaming with the sweet springs. . . . The land is full of minerals and plenty of woods, of which we have a lack in England. There are growing goodly oaks and elms, beech and birch . . . and fir trees in great abundance. The soil is strong and lusty of its own nature."
—Anonymous English writer, early 1600s

The Americas, 1713

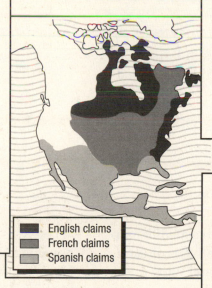

English claims
French claims
Spanish claims

The French Perception

"There is a great number of stags, deer, bears, rabbits, foxes, otters, beavers, weasels, badgers and . . . many other sorts of wild beasts."
—Jacques Cartier, 1530s

The Spanish Perception

"The discovery of the South Sea would lead to the discovery of many islands rich in gold, pearls, precious stones . . . and other unknown and wonderful things."
—Hernán Cortés, 1533

59

Geography and History Activity (continued)

The English, however, found a land and climate in Virginia that was better suited than their homeland for growing food. English colonies of the 1600s grew into farm communities that traded farm products for manufactured English goods.

Different Perceptions

The different ways in which the Spanish, French, and English explored and colonized the Americas reflected their differing perceptions of the regions. Early Spanish explorers were enticed to search for the fabled cities of gold. Their dreams of finding riches gave explorers the determination to face hardships and disappointments. French explorers, however, looked at North America as a place where fortunes could be made from the fur trade. The English valued the rich soil, the game, and the timber.

✔ Applying Geography to History

Directions: Answer the following questions in the spaces provided.

1. **Analyzing** What makes people perceive regions differently?

_____

_____

2. **Stating** What North American resources were important to the Spanish, the French, and the English?

_____

_____

3. **Explaining** What circumstances in Europe made the English so delighted to find good farmland in North America?

_____

_____

4. **Making Inferences** How do you think the English and French points of view may have influenced the early development of their communities?

_____

_____

5. **Finding the Main Idea** State in your own words the main idea of the article.

_____

_____

_____

GOING FURTHER ▶ ▶ ▶ ▶

- Select one of the European expeditions to North America in the late 1400s or early 1500s. Conduct research and write a report describing in detail what type of settlement resulted from the expedition. Where was it, who lived there, and for how long? What were conditions like? How did the Europeans pursue their goals? What were relations like with Native Americans, if present in the area?

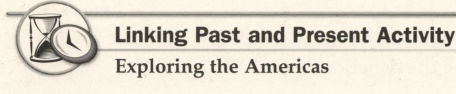

Chapter

Linking Past and Present Activity

Exploring the Americas

Inca Gold

THEN The Inca mined gold throughout their empire. Gold decorated their buildings and clothing. It also played an important role in their worship of the sun god. At the Temple of the Sun in the city of Cuzco, the Sapa Inca, or Inca ruler, ate from gold dishes. Gold covered the walls of some of Cuzco's buildings, and strips of gold were woven through grass roofs to reflect the setting sun.

When the Spanish conquistador Francisco Pizarro arrived on the South American coast, he took the Inca ruler Atahualpa prisoner. Although the Inca paid Pizarro a room full of gold for the ruler's release, Pizarro executed him. Pizarro transported almost all of the Inca gold to Spain. Reports of that gold inspired European voyages to America.

NOW Although the Inca did not use gold as money, today many countries use gold to back up their currency. If a country agrees to buy and sell gold at a fixed price, and if the country's bank has, for instance, a dollar's worth of gold for every dollar it prints, it is said to be "on the gold standard."

Gold also has important industrial uses. Electronics technology uses gold in everything from telephones to washing machines. Some window glass is coated with gold because it can conserve heat. One ounce (28 g) of gold can cover up to 1,000 square feet (93 sq. m) of glass. Satellites and astronauts' visors are also coated with gold because gold reflects most infrared radiation.

1. **Collecting Data** The newspaper's financial pages list the price of gold. Using a chart like the one below, track the price of gold each day for three weeks. In these three weeks, did the price of gold fall or rise? By how much? From this data, would you expect gold to be a stable investment? Why or why not?

The Price of Gold															
	Monday			Tuesday			Wednesday			Thursday			Friday		
Week	1	2	3	1	2	3	1	2	3	1	2	3	1	2	3
Price of Gold															
Amount of Increase or Decrease															
Percentage Change															

2. **Finding the Price of Gold** **DIRECTIONS:** Form a group with three other classmates. Check the financial section of a newspaper for the price of one ounce (28 g) of gold. With your group, create a poster showing the groceries that could be purchased for that price. Display your poster in the classroom.

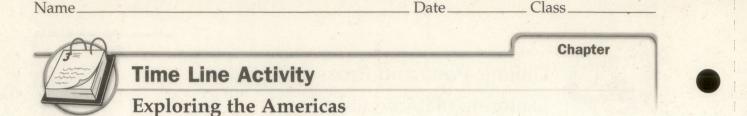

Time Line Activity

Exploring the Americas

Spanish Conquistadors in the Americas

Directions: Use your textbook and the information in the time line to answer the questions in the spaces provided.

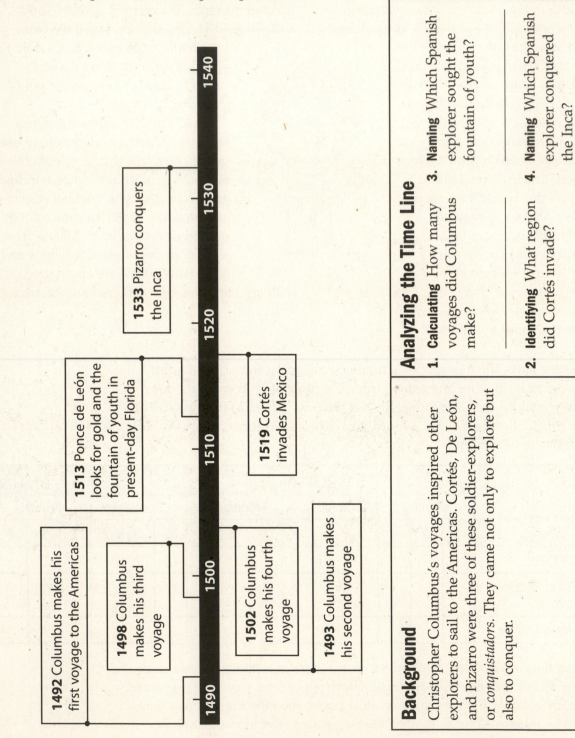

1492 Columbus makes his first voyage to the Americas

1498 Columbus makes his third voyage

1513 Ponce de León looks for gold and the fountain of youth in present-day Florida

1533 Pizarro conquers the Inca

1519 Cortés invades Mexico

1502 Columbus makes his fourth voyage

1493 Columbus makes his second voyage

Background

Christopher Columbus's voyages inspired other explorers to sail to the Americas. Cortés, De León, and Pizarro were three of these soldier-explorers, or *conquistadors*. They came not only to explore but also to conquer.

Analyzing the Time Line

1. **Calculating** How many voyages did Columbus make?

_____

2. **Identifying** What region did Cortés invade?

_____

3. **Naming** Which Spanish explorer sought the fountain of youth?

_____

4. **Naming** Which Spanish explorer conquered the Inca?

_____

School-to-Home Connection Activity

Exploring the Americas

What Do You Know?

Directions: Ask each other the following questions to see how much you know about exploring the Americas.*

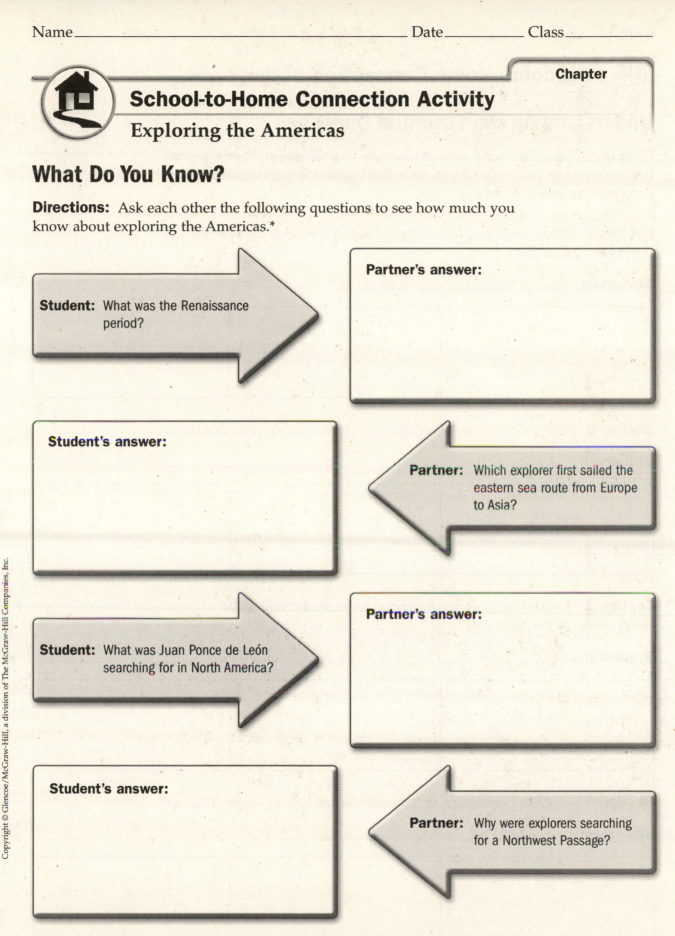

Student: What was the Renaissance period?

Partner's answer:

Student's answer:

Partner: Which explorer first sailed the eastern sea route from Europe to Asia?

Student: What was Juan Ponce de León searching for in North America?

Partner's answer:

Student's answer:

Partner: Why were explorers searching for a Northwest Passage?

*With your student, find answers to these questions in the student textbook.

School-to-Home Connection Activity (continued)

Understanding the Essential Questions

Directions: Rewrite each Essential Question as a statement. Then use your textbook to help you write three details that support your statement in the graphic organizer provided.

Section 1 What events and technological advances paved the way for European exploration?

Statement: _____

Section 2 Why did Spain and Portugal want to find a sea route to Asia?

Statement: _____

Section 3 How did Spain's conquests affect the economic and social development of the Americas?

Statement: _____

Section 4 Why did European nations establish colonies in North America?

Statement: _____

Chapter

Reteaching Activity

Exploring the Americas

By the 1400s, powerful European rulers began to sponsor expeditions to find new trade routes and increase their nation's wealth. The adventurers who led these expeditions often did not find what they sought. However, their explorations added to the knowledge of the world and influenced the course of history in the Americas.

Completing a Sequencing Chart   DIRECTIONS: Each explorer listed below played an important role in the history of the Americas. Write each name next to the date and significance described on the time line.

Amerigo Vespucci   Henry Hudson   John Cabot
Christopher Columbus   Hernán Cortés   Juan Ponce de León
Ferdinand Magellan   Hernando de Soto   Samuel de Champlain
Francisco Pizarro   Jacques Cartier

Explorer	Significance	Date
	1. landed in what is now the Bahamas, giving Europeans their first foothold in the Americas	1492
	2. probably landed on the coast of present-day Newfoundland, giving England a basis for claims in North America	1497
	3. began expedition that mapped the coastline of South America, concluding it was a continent, not part of Asia	1499
	4. landed on the coast of present-day Florida, leading to the first Spanish settlements in what is now the United States	1513
	5. began first circumnavigation of the world, completed by his crew after his death	1519
	6. destroyed the Aztec capital of Tenochtitlán in Mexico, opening the way to Spanish control of the region	1521
	7. captured the Inca ruler in present-day Peru, and within a few years gained control of the vast Inca Empire	1532
	8. sailed up the St. Lawrence River to the site of present-day Montreal	1535
	9. crossed the Mississippi River as part of a three-year exploration of the present-day southeastern United States	1541
	10. began the settlement of Quebec in present-day Canada	1608
	11. sailed along a river that now bears his name, reaching as far north as present-day Albany, New York	1609

Section Resources

Section

Guided Reading Activity

Exploring the Americas

A Changing World

If you need to read a large block of text, use a ruler to help you move from line to line as you read.

Outlining   DIRECTIONS: Reading the section and completing the outline below will help you learn more about the changing world. Refer to your textbook to fill in the blanks.

I. New Nations and Ideas

  A. The_____ brought western Europeans into contact with the Middle East.

  B. Trade grew as the demand for _____, perfumes, and silks from Asia grew.

  C. Citizens studied _____ ancient Greek and Roman works, which led to the period known as the _____.

  D. Strong _____ sought ways to increase trade and make their countries stronger and wealthier.

II. Technology's Impact

  A. More accurate land and sea _____ showed the direction of ocean currents and lines of latitude.

  B. Sailors used _____ to determine their latitude and _____ to determine their direction.

  C. The Portuguese developed the _____, which could sail faster, carry more cargo, and float in shallow water.

III. African Kingdoms

  A. Ghana prospered from _____ imposed on trade.

  B. _____ in Mali became an important center of Islamic art and learning.

  C. The Songhai Empire had laws based on the _____.

Guided Reading Activity

Exploring the Americas

Early Exploration

Reading Tip   Before reading, use visual clues, such as headings, boldfaced terms, and graphics, to figure out what is important in the text.

Reading for Accuracy   **DIRECTIONS:** Use your textbook to decide if a statement is true or false. Write **T** or **F** in the blank. If a statement is false, rewrite it to make it true.

_____ **1.** Henry the Navigator discovered the Cape of Good Hope.

_____

_____ **2.** Vasco de Gama completed the eastern sea route from Portugal to Asia.

_____

_____ **3.** Following Cabral's voyage, Portugal established its first permanent forts in China.

_____

_____ **4.** Christopher Columbus believed he could reach Asia by sailing west.

_____

_____ **5.** Columbus found a sponsor in Italy to finance his voyage.

_____

_____ **6.** Columbus thought he had reached the Americas in 1492, but instead he had reached the East Indies.

_____

_____ **7.** The Treaty of Tordesillas divided the unexplored world between Spain and Portugal.

_____

Guided Reading Activity

Exploring the Americas

Spain in America

Reading Tip When you finish reading the text below a heading, make sure you under-stand its main idea. If not, reread the text.

Answering Questions   **DIRECTIONS:** As you read the section, answer the questions below.

1. **Identifying** What did the conquistadors receive from Spanish rulers?

_____

_____

2. **Locating** The conquering of the Aztec Empire by Cortés gave Spain control of land in what present-day country?

_____

3. **Naming** Which conquistador gained control of the Inca Empire?

_____

4. **Listing** List three reasons why the conquistadors were able to conquer the Aztec and Inca Empires.

_____

_____

5. **Specifying** Where and when did Ponce de León make the first Spanish landing on the North American mainland?

_____

6. **Explaining** What inspired de Soto to lead an expedition to the west?

_____

7. **Determining Cause and Effect** What effect did the giving of encomienda to conquistadors have on Native Americans?

_____

8. **Analyzing** What system brought slave labor to the colonies?

_____

Guided Reading Activity

Exploring the Americas

Exploring North America

Reading Tip

As you read, pause and ask yourself some questions, such as "What do I think about this?" or "Why is this so?"

Filling in the Blanks   **DIRECTIONS:** Use your textbook to fill in the blanks using the words in the box. Use another sheet of paper if necessary.

resources	Jacques Cartier	mercantilism
Northwest Passage	Columbian Exchange	fur trading
Protestant Reformation	Henry Hudson	Martin Luther
New Netherland	coureurs de bois	John Cabot

The religious movement known as the **(1)** _____ began with the protests of

(2) _____ against the Catholic Church. Religious divisions then spread throughout

Europe and the Americas.

The theory of **(3)** _____ is that a nation's power is based on its wealth.

European countries competed for colonies in the Americas that would provide valuable

(4) _____ to increase their wealth. The voyages of explorers between Europe,

Asia, Africa, and the Americas led to transfers of plants, animals, and diseases known as

the **(5)** _____. To speed the voyage to Asia, many explorers hoped to find a direct

water route through the Americas, known as the **(6)** _____. Some who tried were

English explorer **(7)** _____ and French explorer **(8)** _____.

(9) _____ discovered the river and bay that bears his name during his travels. The

French focused on earning wealth in North America from fishing and **(10)** _____.

They built trading posts to collect furs from trappers who were known as

(11) _____. Dutch exploration led to the establishment of the colony of

(12) _____, whose center is today known as New York City.

Chapter Resources

Colonial America

Chapter

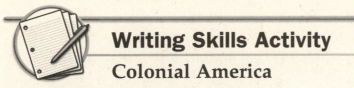

Writing Skills Activity

Colonial America

Writing Parallel Structures

✓ Learning the Skill

"My favorite hobbies are skateboarding, baking, and reading."

"He cleaned his room, walked the dog, and finished his homework."

The sentences above are examples of parallel structures. Parallel structures use the same pattern of words to show that two or more ideas have the same level of importance. They make your writing more concise and easier to follow. The usual way to join parallel structures is with the use of coordinating conjunctions such as *and* and *or*.

Follow these steps in using parallel structure:

- Skim your paper, pausing at the words *and* or *or*. Check to see whether the items joined are parallel. If not, alter them to create a parallel.

- Make sure verbs are consistent in tense (such as *jumped* and *shouted*).

- Use articles (such as *the*) with every item in a series or only with the first item in the series.

- If you have several items in a list, put them in columns to see if they are parallel.

- Listen to the sound of the items in a list or the items being compared. Do you hear the same kinds of sounds? For example, is there a series of *-ing* words that begin each item? Do you hear a rhythm that is being repeated? If something is breaking the rhythm or repetition of the sound, check to see if it needs to be made parallel.

✓ Practicing the Skill

Directions: Read each pair of sentences below and on the next page. Circle the sentence that uses correct parallel structure.

1. **A.** The toddler swung on the swings, climbs on the monkey bars, and slid down the slides.

   B. The toddler swung on the swings, climbed on the monkey bars, and slid down the slides.

2. **A.** She likes listening to country music and reading mystery novels.

   B. She likes listening to country music and to read mystery novels.

Writing Skills Activity (continued)

3. **A.** I want to paint my bedroom, hang new posters, and the new curtains need to be bought.

   B. I want to paint my bedroom, hang new posters, and buy new curtains.

4. **A.** Andrew spent his days attending classes, studying, and working at the grocery store.

   B. Andrew spent his days attending classes, studying, and he worked at the grocery store.

✔ Applying the Skill

Directions: Read each sentence below. Then rewrite the sentence using parallel structure.

1. Spanish missions were set up in New Mexico, in Texas, California, and in other areas of North America.

   _____

2. Some enslaved Africans learned trades such as blacksmithing and to weave.

   _____

3. Junipero Serra was born in 1713, in 1749 he left Spain, and he established a mission in San Diego in 1769.

   _____

   _____

4. While most Spanish colonists settled in the Caribbean, Mexico, and Central America, most French and English colonies were in North America.

   _____

   _____

Self-Assessment Checklist

Assess your sentences using the checklist below:

☐ I joined parallel structures with *and* or *or.*

☐ I used consistent verb forms or adjectives.

☐ I used articles at the start or with every item in the series.

☐ I listened to the sound of items in the list.

Chapter

Social Studies Skills Activity

Colonial America

Reading a Bar Graph

☑ Learning the Skill

Bar graphs allow you to compare quantities at a glance. Each bar represents an amount—the longer the bar is, the larger the amount is. Bars can be either vertical (up and down) or horizontal (left to right).

A bar graph provides information along two sides, or axes, of the graph. The *horizontal axis* is the line across the bottom of the graph. What you are comparing is usually labeled there. The *vertical axis* is the line along the side. It usually has numbers, and you measure the lengths of the bars with these numbers.

To read a bar graph, follow these steps:

- Read the title to find out the subject of the bar graph.
- Study the information on the side and bottom of the graph to figure out what the bars represent.
- Compare the lengths of the bars to draw conclusions about the graph's topic.

☑ Practicing the Skill

Directions: The bar graph below shows the population of the American colonies from 1680 through 1730. Read the graph, and then answer the questions that follow.

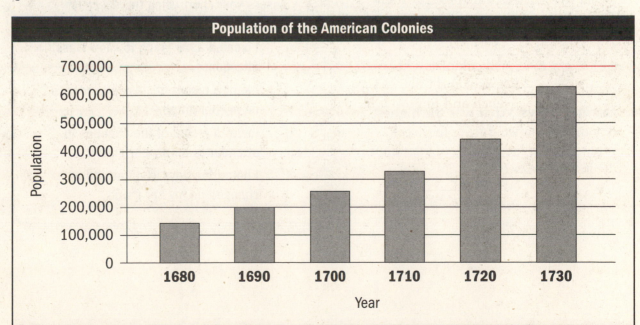

Name_____ Date_____ Class_____

 Social Studies Skills Activity (continued)

1. **Analyzing Visuals** What is the subject of this bar graph?

_____

2. **Identifying** What was the population of the colonies in 1690?

_____

3. **Calculating** About how much did the colonial population increase between 1700 and 1710?

_____

4. **Identifying** Between what years did the biggest increase occur?

_____

✔ Applying the Skill

Directions: On a separate sheet of paper, make a bar graph showing class attendance for each day of the week. Record how many students are present in your class for one week. Then follow the directions below.

1. **Calculating** How many students were in attendance from Tuesday to Friday?

_____

2. **Analyzing Visuals** When was the greatest difference in attendance for the week? When was the least difference in attendance during the week?

_____

_____

3. **Analyzing Visuals** What was the highest day of attendance during the week? What was the lowest day of attendance during the week?

_____

_____

Self-Assessment Checklist

Assess your chart using the checklist below:

- ☐ I created a bar graph to show class attendance.
- ☐ I kept a record of class attendance on my bar graph.
- ☐ I kept a record of the changes in attendance on my bar graph.
- ☐ I noted the days when attendance changed on my bar graph.

Differentiated Instruction Activity

Colonial America

Hex Signs of the Pennsylvania Dutch

In the late 1600s and early 1700s, groups of Amish, Mennonite, and Lutheran immigrants from Germany came to southeastern Pennsylvania. Known as the Pennsylvania Dutch, they brought many of their traditions and beliefs with them. One tradition involved the creation of designs that decorated marriage and birth certificates, Bibles, furniture, and quilts. Designs incorporating six-pointed stars were especially common. Because the pronunciation of the German word for *six* (sechs) sounded like the English word *hex*, these designs eventually became known as "hex signs." Hex signs can still be seen throughout Pennsylvania.

By the 1830s, many Pennsylvania Dutch farmers were painting their barns and decorating their homes with hex signs. Families attached a wide variety of meanings to the designs and symbols, some of which are listed in the following table. The origins of many of these designs and symbols can be traced to medieval Europe.

Symbol	Meaning
distelfink (bird)	good luck and happiness; two distelfinks crossed over each other means true friendship
heart	true love, lasting love, love for others
pineapple	welcome and hospitality
stars	good luck, hope, love, fertility
tulips	faith, hope, charity
Color	**Meaning**
blue	protection, peace
white	purity
green	abundance, growth, fertility
brown	earth, friendship, strength

Directions: Use the information from the excerpt and your textbook to answer the following questions on a separate sheet of paper.

1. **Explaining** Who were the Pennsylvania Dutch?

2. **Analyzing** What is one theme or idea that you see expressed in some of the symbols used in the hex signs? Why do you think this theme was important to the Pennsylvania Dutch? Explain your answer.

Differentiated Instruction Activity (continued)

Teaching Strategies for Different Learning Styles

The following activities are ways the basic lesson can be modified to accommodate students' different learning styles.

English Language Learner (ELL)

Have students answer the following questions about the passage: (1) What are hex signs? (2) What group of people introduced hex signs to Pennsylvania? (3) Name one shape often used in hex signs. (4) How did "hex signs" get their name?

Special Needs

Using visuals of the hex signs, review the passage with students, explaining the concept of *symbolism* as needed. Pass around to students some green plants and bowls/jars of soil, and prompt them to volunteer explanations for why the color green symbolizes growth and the color brown represents earth. Ask them what colors they might choose to symbolize water or the sun.

Gifted and Talented

Like the Pennsylvania Dutch, most immigrants to America typically bring with them traditions distinctive to their native cultures. Ask students to explore other examples of cultural diffusion and develop a class presentation or multimedia display of their findings.

Verbal/Linguistic; Intrapersonal

Ask students to write a two- to three-page paper about various symbols—religious, corporate, and so forth—in use today. Students' reports should describe the symbols and explain their meaning.

Logical/Mathematical

Ask students to use library and Internet resources to create a three-column table categorizing the symbols used in hex signs. Column titles should be *Name of Symbol, Illustration of Symbol,* and *Meaning of Symbol.*

Illustrations of each symbol should be included in the tables.

Visual/Spatial

Have students use library and Internet resources to learn about other symbols and colors used in hex signs, and then have them design their own. Ask them to explain the meaning of their designs in a paragraph or two.

Kinesthetic; Verbal/Linguistic; Interpersonal

Ask student pairs to research the Pennsylvania Dutch dialect (aka Pennsylvania German or Deitsch) and find examples of distinctive words, proverbs, or phrases. Then have them write a brief skit, each line of which should contain a word or phrase of Pennsylvania Dutch. Ask pairs to perform their skit for the class. Afterward, query the audience to discover if the dialogue was understood.

Naturalist

Point out to students that hex signs are based on nature using special symbols that stand for different things. Ask students to create their own table of symbols and meanings from natural objects.

Below Grade Level

Provide each student with two hex signs, and have students create a Venn diagram comparing and contrasting the two.

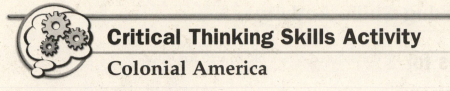

Chapter

Critical Thinking Skills Activity
Colonial America

Analyzing Information

✔ Learning the Skill

Analyzing information involves distinguishing fact from opinion and checking for statements that you can verify. Primary sources are often first-person accounts of someone who witnessed an event. The passage that follows is from the diary of Brother Cammerhoff, a man who traveled through the backcountry of what is now the state of New York in 1750.

> We had a worse road than we had on the whole Journey. The Indian guide told us . . . that we would have to pass over a bad road, and if he said the road was bad, it must certainly be very bad. Thus far we had at least been able to travel on the ground, but now we went through swamps and marshes, where the flies troubled us greatly. For miles we were obliged to walk on trees and branches, as on both sides were deep marshes . . . [and] we sometimes slipped from the trees . . . and fell into the swamp, and could scarcely get up again with our heavy bundles. . . . Toward evening we reached an old Indian settlement where a city by the name of Onnache is said to have stood. . . . We were caught in a dreadful thunder and rain storm, and were thoroughly drenched, particularly in going through the tall grass. We went a little farther and encamped along a creek called Otochshiaco. . . . We tried to dry ourselves at the fire . . . and went to sleep, feeling cold and wet.

Source: Brother Cammerhoff, *Moravian Journals Relating to Central New York*, 1745–1766 (W.M. Beauchamp, ed.). Syracuse, NY: 1916.

✔ Practicing the Skill

Directions: Use the passage to answer the following questions.

1. **Identifying** What is the primary source for this passage?

_____

2. **Specifying** What did you learn about traveling the back roads of early America by reading this passage?

_____

_____

3. **Interpreting** What part of the passage suggests that Native Americans had lived in the area for a long time?

_____

_____

Critical Thinking Skills Activity (continued)

4. **Evaluating** Why would the diary be considered a reliable source for information?

_____

_____

_____

5. **Recognizing Bias** What parts of this source might make it unreliable? Explain your answer.

_____

_____

_____

✓ Applying the Skill

Directions: In the blank at the left, write the letter of the choice that best answers the question.

_____ 1. In what type of natural environment was the writer traveling?

    A. desert oasis   **C.** ocean shore

    B. swamp and forest   **D.** prairie grassland

_____ 2. What was the writer's attitude toward his Native American guide?

    A. The writer distrusted him.

    B. The writer was fond of him.

    C. The writer displayed no particular attitude toward him.

    D. The writer was grateful to him for saving his life.

_____ 3. Which of the following statements is probably true of the writer?

    A. He was a native of the area through which he was traveling.

    B. He was a Native American.

    C. He enjoyed his journey.

    D. He was not used to traveling by foot through a dense forest.

_____ 4. What other type of primary source would reveal the personal experiences of someone who lived long ago?

    A. letters   **C.** newspaper articles on politics

    B. shipping receipts   **D.** prayer books

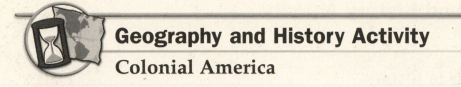

Chapter

Geography and History Activity
Colonial America

Colonizing North America

By the mid-1700s, British settlers had been colonizing the United States for almost a century and a half. Hoping to profit from resources discovered in North America, the British established colonies up and down the east coast: New Hampshire, Massachusetts, Rhode Island and Providence Plantation, Connecticut, New York, New Jersey, Pennsylvania, Delaware, Maryland, Virginia, North and South Carolina, and Georgia.

The British were not the only Europeans colonizing North America. The French and Spanish also established settlements elsewhere on the continent. In fact, the British government created Georgia, located between Spanish Florida and South Carolina, in part to protect other colonies from attacks by Spain. Conflicts between Britain and Spain over new territories were frequent.

Spain was determined to protect its holdings on the continent, which included most of Mexico, Central America, and part of the western and southern present-day United States. Spanish priests set up a string of missions along the Pacific coast, allowing them to claim California as well. These missions grew into cities like Los Angeles and San Diego.

The French, who founded Quebec in 1608, initially were not keen on colonizing America. Their interest lay in profits from fur trade and fishing. But the possibility of discovering gold and silver, and a water passage to the Pacific Ocean, lured the French to send explorers Joliet and Marquette down the Mississippi River. Once they realized it flowed south into the Gulf of Mexico instead of west, they turned back. France eventually claimed Louisiana, and sent missionaries and explorers west to the Rocky Mountains and southwest to the Rio Grande River. France also had settlements along the St. Lawrence River in New France in present-day Canada.

French colonies grew so slowly that many Native Americans were not forced from their lands. This was not true in the rapidly expanding British colonies, where settlers and Native Americans fought fiercely for the land.

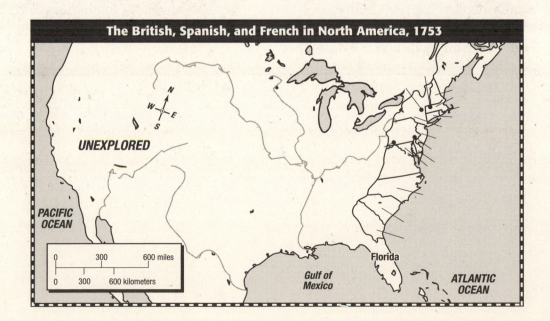

The British, Spanish, and French in North America, 1753

UNEXPLORED

PACIFIC OCEAN

0   300   600 miles
0   300   600 kilometers

Gulf of Mexico

Florida

ATLANTIC OCEAN

Geography and History Activity (continued)

✓ Applying Geography to History

Directions: Write or draw on the map to answer questions 1–5. You may abbreviate if you wish.

1. **Illustrating** Color with different colors the regions claimed by the British, French, and Spanish. Label each region with the name of the appropriate country.

2. **Labeling** Write the name of each of the thirteen British colonies on the map.

3. **Contrasting** Describe two differences in the way Britain and France colonized North America.

   _____

   _____

   _____

4. **Locating** Write the names of the following rivers on the map: Mississippi, Rio Grande, St. Lawrence.

5. **Calculating** Use the map scale to figure out the length of the Mississippi River to its mouth. Draw a line between the two places and write the appropriate distance on the line.

GOING FURTHER ▶ ▶▶▶

- Conduct research on the 21 missions established by Spain in California. Create a map showing the locations of each of the missions and the dates they were founded. Also indicate the cities that grew from those missions and the dates they were incorporated.

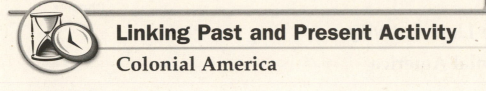

Linking Past and Present Activity
Colonial America

Popular Rule

THEN Jamestown, the first successful English colony in North America, was financed by the Virginia Company of London. Many early Jamestown settlers belonged to the English aristocracy. They came to America seeking fortunes, but their lives in England had not prepared them to survive in the wilderness. As a result, the colony almost failed.

These early colonists identified themselves as English subjects and expected their government to be headed by a monarch. By 1619, however, many Jamestown colonists demanded changes. To deal with colonists' complaints, the Virginia Company appointed a governor but allowed the colonists to elect representatives to a House of Burgesses. The Virginia Company failed in 1624, but the colonists petitioned King Charles I to allow them to keep their elected assembly. Finally, in 1638, the king told the colony's governor to call the assembly into session every year.

NOW Giving the people a say in their government turned out to be something that Americans would never give up. In the United States today, the right to vote is a widely cherished principle. It is the basis for democracy. All American citizens 18 years or older have the right to cast a ballot for candidates of their choice. The winners then represent them in making laws and determining policies. If elected officials do not adequately represent the people who elected them, they can be removed from office at the next election.

In 1993 Congress passed the "motor-voter" bill, which makes voter registration easier by allowing registration by mail or at the time drivers' licenses are granted or renewed. The bill's authors hoped to encourage more voter participation in elections. The law took effect in 1995.

Unfortunately, many eligible voters still fail to register and to vote in presidential elections. The chart below shows some recent examples.

1. Researching Voting Statistics Use the library or Internet to discover voting statistics for past elections. Complete the chart below with the data you find.

Voting in Recent Presidential Elections			
	Number of Citizens of Voting Age	Number of Citizens Who Voted	Percentage of Voting Age Citizens Who Voted
1996			
2000	186,366,000	110,826,000	59.5
2004			

2. Writing a Letter You hold a seat in the House of Burgesses. King Charles I does not want to give the House legal status. On a separate sheet of paper, write a letter to persuade him to do so.

Time Line Activity
Colonial America

Colonial Governments in America

Directions: Use the following information about colonial America to create your own time line.

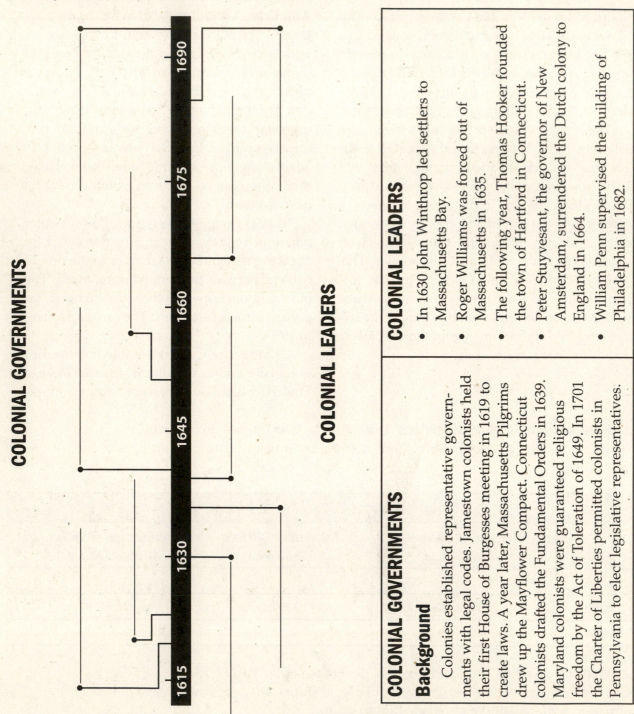

COLONIAL GOVERNMENTS

1615 1630 1645 1660 1675 1690

COLONIAL LEADERS

COLONIAL LEADERS

- In 1630 John Winthrop led settlers to Massachusetts Bay.
- Roger Williams was forced out of Massachusetts in 1635.
- The following year, Thomas Hooker founded the town of Hartford in Connecticut.
- Peter Stuyvesant, the governor of New Amsterdam, surrendered the Dutch colony to England in 1664.
- William Penn supervised the building of Philadelphia in 1682.

COLONIAL GOVERNMENTS
Background

Colonies established representative governments with legal codes. Jamestown colonists held their first House of Burgesses meeting in 1619 to create laws. A year later, Massachusetts Pilgrims drew up the Mayflower Compact. Connecticut colonists drafted the Fundamental Orders in 1639. Maryland colonists were guaranteed religious freedom by the Act of Toleration of 1649. In 1701 the Charter of Liberties permitted colonists in Pennsylvania to elect legislative representatives.

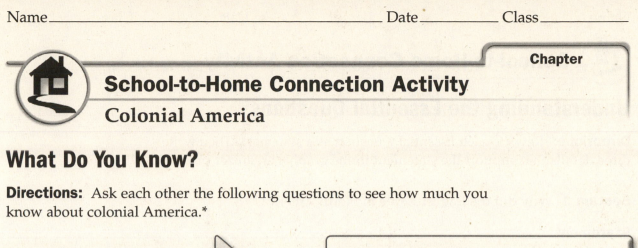

Chapter

School-to-Home Connection Activity
Colonial America

What Do You Know?

Directions: Ask each other the following questions to see how much you know about colonial America.*

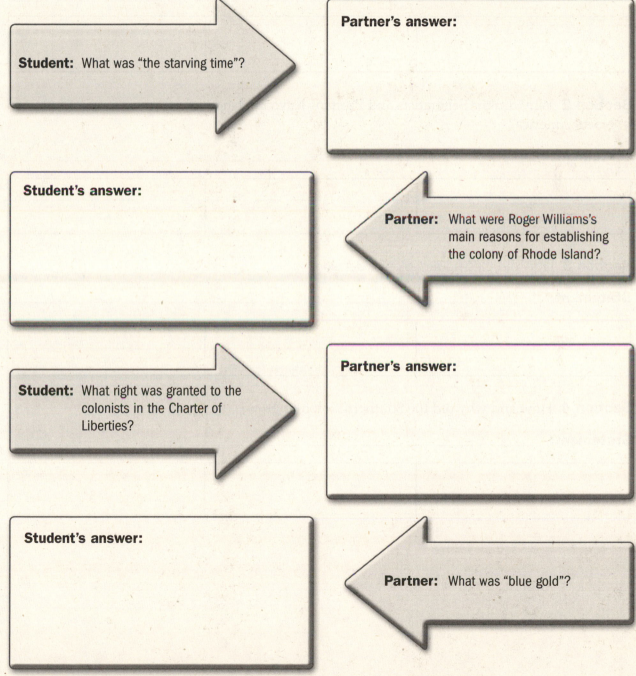

Student: What was "the starving time"?

Partner's answer:

Student's answer:

Partner: What were Roger Williams's main reasons for establishing the colony of Rhode Island?

Student: What right was granted to the colonists in the Charter of Liberties?

Partner's answer:

Student's answer:

Partner: What was "blue gold"?

*With your student, find answers to these questions in the student textbook.

School-to-Home Connection Activity (continued)

Understanding the Essential Questions

Directions: Rewrite each Essential Question as a statement. Then write three details that support the statement in the graphic organizer provided.

Section 1 Why did the English settle in North America?

Statement: _____

Section 2 Why did the Separatists and Puritans leave England and settle in North America?

Statement: _____

Section 3 How did the Middle Colonies develop?

Statement: _____

Section 4 How and why did the Southern Colonies grow?

Statement: _____

Reteaching Activity
Colonial America

Settlers came to America for many reasons. Some sought the freedom to worship as they pleased. Others came seeking land, profit, or a fresh start in life. These diverse settlers established America's thirteen colonies.

Organizing Information   DIRECTIONS: From the list below, write the name of each colony in the appropriate box in the diagram. Then write the name of the colony's leaders or founders. Write an asterisk (*) next to each colony that was founded mainly as a safe place to practice a religion.

Colonies

Connecticut
Delaware
Georgia
Maryland
Massachusetts (Plymouth
  & Massachusetts Bay Colony)
New Hampshire
New Jersey
New York
North Carolina
Pennsylvania
Rhode Island
South Carolina
Virginia

Founders or Leaders

Cecilius Calvert
Dutch settlers
George Carteret
group of eight aristocrats
James Oglethorpe
John Berkeley
John Smith
John Wheelwright
John Winthrop
William Bradford
Roger Williams
Swedish settlers
Thomas Hooker
William Penn

America's Thirteen Colonies

New England Colonies	Founders or Leaders
_____	_____
_____	_____
_____	_____
_____	_____

Middle Colonies	Founders or Leaders
_____	_____
_____	_____
_____	_____
_____	_____

Southern Colonies	Founders or Leaders
_____	_____
_____	_____
_____	_____
_____	_____

Section Resources

Guided Reading Activity

Guided Reading Activity

Guided Reading Activity

Guided Reading Activity

Section

Guided Reading Activity

Colonial America

Early English Settlements

Reading Tip Give yourself enough time to read and understand the text. Don't rush through it. Take your time and pause to reread sections or to think about what you've just read.

Filling in the Blanks **DIRECTIONS:** Use your textbook to fill in the blanks using the words in the box. Use another sheet of paper if necessary.

Sir Walter Raleigh	House of Burgesses	royal	Roanoke
Captain John Smith	Spanish Armada	seas	Virginia Company
Sir Francis Drake	colonists	England	charters
John White	tobacco	Jamestown	

Trading rivalry and religious differences pushed **(1)** _____ and Spain toward war.

(2) _____ attacked Spanish ships and ports. King Philip II sent the **(3)**

_____ to conquer England, but it failed. This marked the end of Spanish

control of the **(4)** _____.

Queen Elizabeth gave **(5)** _____ the right to claim land in North America.

He sent people to settle in **(6)** _____, led by **(7)** _____. He returned

to England for supplies, and when he finally returned to the settlement found it deserted. The

(8) _____ were never seen again.

Groups of merchants sought **(9)** _____ to settle in North America. The **(10)**

_____ was a joint-stock company that sent colonists who settled **(11)**

_____. **(12)** _____ helped the colonists survive the first two

years. They eventually found a way to make money by growing **(13)** _____.

Colonists formed the **(14)** _____, where representatives made laws for the colony.

Due to financial trouble, King James canceled the charter in 1624, and Jamestown

became the first **(15)** _____ colony in America.

Guided Reading Activity

Colonial America

New England Colonies

Reading Tip Use self-adhesive notes to flag main ideas, important events, or areas in the text that you may need to reread for better understanding.

Answering Questions   DIRECTIONS: As you read the section, answer the questions below.

1. **Differentiating** What was the difference between Puritans and Separatists?

_____

2. **Stating** Who are the two groups of people the word *Pilgrims* could apply to?

_____

_____

3. **Identifying** Where did the *Mayflower's* passengers end up going ashore?

_____

4. **Analyzing** Why was the Mayflower Compact a step in the development of representative government in America?

_____

5. **Naming** Which Native Americans helped the Pilgrims grow and hunt for food, and make peace with the Wampanoag?

_____

6. **Describing** What was the Great Migration?

_____

_____

7. **Defining** What was the Fundamental Orders of Connecticut?

_____

_____

Guided Reading Activity

Colonial America

Middle Colonies

Reading Tip

It is important to focus on your reading assignment. Make time to read this section and pay attention to it as you read.

Outlining DIRECTIONS: Reading the section and completing the outline below will help you learn more about the Middle Colonies. Refer to your textbook to fill in the blanks.

I. England and the Colonies

   A. In 1660 England had two clusters of colonies in the north and south;

   between them were lands controlled by the _____.

   B. The New Netherland colony had a thriving _____ trade, which caused the English to want to acquire the colony.

   C. England sent a fleet to attack in 1664; the governor, _____, was unprepared for battle and surrendered the colony.

   D. King Charles gave the colony to the Duke of York, who renamed

   it _____.

   E. The colony became a _____ colony, in which the

   owner controlled the _____ and owned all the land.

   F. The southern part of the colony was given to proprietors who

   named it _____ and who promised freedom of religion, trial by jury, and a representative assembly.

II. Pennsylvania

   A. _____ received the colony as payment for a debt.

   B. He saw the opportunity to put _____—pacifists who believed everyone was equal—ideals into practice here.

   C. _____ had originally settled southern Pennsylvania, and they were allowed to operate as a separate colony known as

   _____ under Pennsylvania's governor.

Guided Reading Activity

Colonial America

Southern Colonies

Reading Tip   Locate the boldface key terms in this section before you read. Note their meanings before you read the passage.

Reading for Accuracy   DIRECTIONS: Use your textbook to decide if a statement is true or false. Write **T** or **F** in the blank. If a statement is false, rewrite it to make it true.

_____ 1. Indentured servants paid for their passage to America by agreeing to work without pay for a certain amount of time.

_____

_____ 2. The Mason-Dixon line established the boundary between Maryland and Virginia.

_____

_____ 3. William Berkeley rebelled against Nathaniel Bacon's pledge to keep settlers from moving into Native American territory.

_____

_____ 4. Two important crops grown in Carolina were rice and indigo.

_____

_____ 5. The last British colony to set up in America was South Carolina.

_____

_____ 6. In Georgia, forts and the town of Savannah were built as a barrier against French expansion.

_____

_____ 7. Louis Joliet and Jácques Marquette followed the Mississippi River to the Gulf of Mexico and claimed the region for France.

_____

_____ 8. Tenant farmers were settlers who paid their lord an annual rent and worked for him a fixed number of days per year.

_____

_____ 9. Missions are religious settlements established to convert people to a faith.

_____

Growth of the Thirteen Colonies

Content Vocabulary Activity

Growth of the Thirteen Colonies

Matching DIRECTIONS: Write each term below on the line next to its correct definition.

subsistence farming	Tidewater	proprietary colony
triangular trade	backcountry	royal colony
Middle Passage	overseer	Iroquois Confederacy
cash crop	export	militia
slave code	import	alliance
surplus	charter colony	speculator

_____ **1.** Goods bought from foreign markets

_____ **2.** The sea voyage when enslaved Africans were shipped to the West Indies

_____ **3.** A group of civilians trained to fight in the military

_____ **4.** A union between countries or groups of people

_____ **5.** To produce just enough to meet a family's needs, with little left over to sell or exchange

_____ **6.** Strict rules that governed the behavior and punishment of enslaved Africans

_____ **7.** A colony ruled by an individual or a group to whom Britain granted land

_____ **8.** Routes followed by colonial merchant ships

_____ **9.** Investors who owned shares in land companies

_____ **10.** A colony that elected its own governors and the members of its legislature

_____ **11.** Produce grown by farmers for sale in colonial markets and overseas

_____ **12.** Extra amounts of a product

_____ **13.** A colony in which the king appointed a governor and members of the council

_____ **14.** The most powerful group of Native Americans in the East

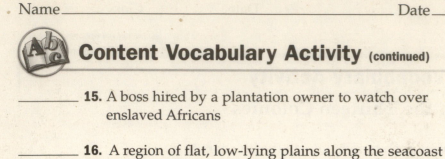

Content Vocabulary Activity (continued)

_____ **15.** A boss hired by a plantation owner to watch over enslaved Africans

_____ **16.** A region of flat, low-lying plains along the seacoast

_____ **17.** Goods that are sold abroad

_____ **18.** A region of hills and forests west of the Tidewater

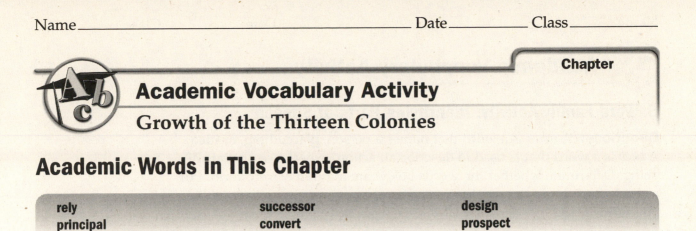

Academic Vocabulary Activity

Growth of the Thirteen Colonies

Academic Words in This Chapter

rely	successor	design
principal	convert	prospect

A. Word Meaning Activity: Identifying Synonyms and Antonyms

Directions: *Synonyms* are words with similar meanings, and *antonyms* are words with opposite meanings. Determine whether the following pairs of words or phrases are synonyms or antonyms. Place an "S" in the blank if the words are synonyms and an "A" if they are antonyms.

_____ **1.** rely—depend

_____ **2.** principal—minor

_____ **3.** successor—leader

_____ **4.** convert—talk out of

_____ **5.** design—plan

_____ **6.** prospect—opportunity

Academic Vocabulary Activity (continued)

B. Word Family Activity: Identifying Parts of Speech

Directions: A *noun* is a word that names a person, place, thing, or idea. A *verb* is a word that is used to describe an action, experience, or state of being. Determine whether the words below are in noun or verb form. Put a check mark (√) in the appropriate column. Some words have more than one form.

Word	Noun	Verb
1. relied		
2. successor		
3. succeed		
4. convert		
5. converted		
6. conversion		
7. involvement		
8. principal		
9. design		
10. designed		
11. prospect		

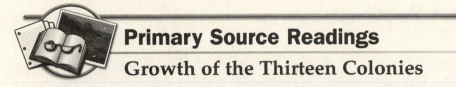

Chapter

Primary Source Readings

Growth of the Thirteen Colonies

Benjamin Franklin and the First Library

Interpreting the Source

Benjamin Franklin had so many interests we often forget that he started the first subscription library in the United States. In 1731 he gathered a group of eager readers in Philadelphia to propose his idea. More than 50 years later, he wrote about that meeting in his autobiography.

Guided Reading

As you read this passage from Franklin's autobiography, think about what Franklin hoped to achieve.

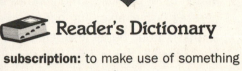

Reader's Dictionary

subscription: to make use of something on a prepayment plan

tradesman: a person who uses his or her hands to do a job, such as a printer, carpenter, or painter

annum: a year

promissory note: written statements promising to make payments

Continuation of the Account of My Life

At the time I established myself in Pennsylvania there was not a good bookseller's shop in any of the colonies to the southward of Boston. . . . Those who loved reading were obliged to send for their books from England; the members of the Junto [a club formed by Franklin in Philadelphia] had each a few. We had left the alehouse where we first met and hired a room to hold our club in. I proposed that we should all of us bring our books to that room, where they would not only be ready to consult in our conferences, but become a common benefit, each of us being at liberty to borrow such as he wished to read at home. This was accordingly done and for some time contented us.

Finding the advantage of this little collection, I proposed to render the benefit from books more common, by commencing a public **subscription** library. I drew a sketch of the plan and rules . . . by which each subscriber engaged to pay a certain sum down for the first purchase of books and an annual contribution for increasing them. So few were the readers at that time in Philadelphia and the majority of us so poor that I was not able with great industry to find more than fifty persons, mostly young **tradesmen**, willing to pay down for this purpose forty shillings each and ten shillings per **annum**. On this little fund we began. The books were imported; the library was opened one day in the week for lending to

Primary Source Readings (continued)

Continuation of the Account of My Life (continued)

the subscribers on their **promissory notes** to pay double the value if not duly returned. The institution soon manifested its utility, was imitated by other towns and in other provinces. The libraries were augmented by donations; reading became fashionable; and our people . . . in a few years were observed by strangers to be better instructed and more intelligent than people of the same rank generally are in other countries.

Source: "Continuation of the Account of My Life, Begun at Passy, Near Paris, 1784"; from *The Autobiography of Benjamin Franklin*

DBQ Document-Based Questions

Directions: Answer the questions below in the spaces provided.

1. **Locating** Where were the bookshops located when Franklin was a young man?

_____

_____

2. **Summarizing** Summarize how Franklin launched his first book sharing group.

_____

_____

3. **Making Inferences** Think about the passage where Franklin talks about their "little fund." Write an explanation for the word *shilling*.

_____

_____

4. **Drawing Conclusions** How do you know that Franklin's library was successful?

_____

_____

5. **Speculating** Read Franklin's final statement in the passage. Then write a statement speculating whether you think this is true of Americans today.

_____

_____

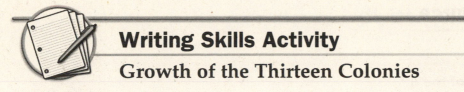

Writing Skills Activity

Growth of the Thirteen Colonies

Outlining

✓ Learning the Skill

Have you ever watched an artist sketch a subject? The artist outlines the design, giving shape to what will soon be filled with color. A good writer also creates an outline, or a skeleton of the main points and supporting points, before beginning to write.

Use the following guidelines to create an outline:

- Read through your source material, and take notes about the subject.
- Organize your notes into a few main topics. Use Roman numerals (I., II., III. etc.) to label main headings.
- Scan the material for subtopics. Subtopics are written as capital letters (A., B., C. etc.).
- Under subtopics, place related details that support the subtopics. Use Arabic numerals (1., 2., 3. etc.) for these details.
- An "A." subtopic should always be followed by a "B." subtopic.
- A "1." detail should always be followed by a "2." detail.
- Use few words, but still express the main idea of the material.

✓ Practicing the Skill

Directions: Study this partial outline, and then answer the questions that follow.

  I. The British

    A. in Europe

    B. in America

  II. The French

    A. in Europe

    B. in America

1. Analyzing What are the two main topics in this outline?

_____

2. Organizing If you were to add two details about the French interacting with Native Americans, where would you place them? Would you use numbers or letters?

_____

_____

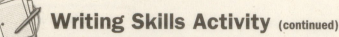

Writing Skills Activity (continued)

✓ Applying the Skill

Directions: Suppose you are in the process of writing a report on the Albany Plan of Union. You have researched information on the topic and gathered details on the note cards shown below. Review the note cards, and then answer the questions that follow.

Finance

Central government can collect taxes, regulate trade, and appoint a General Treasurer and a Particular Treasurer in each government.

Native Americans

Central government can purchase lands from Native Americans, regulate Native Americans trade.

Defense

Central government can raise troops, build forts, arm ships to guard coasts, all military officers nominated by President-General.

1. **Listing** Suppose you list Defense as Roman numeral III in an outline. Name at least two subtopics to list as points A and B.

   _____

   _____

2. **Applying** Research information about the Iroquois Confederacy or Fort Necessity. Write details on note cards. Then, on a separate sheet of paper, write an outline you could use to draft a report on your topic.

Self-Assessment Checklist

Assess your outline using the checklist below:

☐ I wrote details on note cards.

☐ I organized details before writing an outline.

☐ I used Roman numerals for main topics.

☐ I used capital letters for subtopics.

☐ I used Arabic numerals for supporting points.

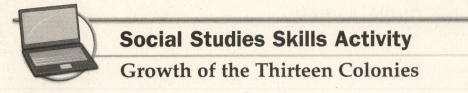

Social Studies Skills Activity

Growth of the Thirteen Colonies

Reading a Table

✓ Learning the Skill

Learning to read tables helps you compare information in an organized way. Tables have two or more columns and rows.

Follow these steps to read a table:

- Read the table title to find out the subject of the table.
- Read the titles at the top of each column.
- Read the information on the side of each row.
- Study and compare the information in the columns and rows. To compare information in one row at a time, read across each row. To compare information in one column at a time, read down each column.

✓ Practicing the Skill

Directions: The table below organizes information in three columns. The table compares and contrasts charter colonies and proprietary colonies. The first column lists the type of colony. The second column lists the features of each type of colony. The third column lists an example of that type of colony. Study the table. Then read and answer the following questions.

Different Kinds of Early American Colonies		
Type	**Features**	**Example**
Charter	rights and privileges granted by British monarchy to stockholders	Rhode Island
Proprietary	owned by individual proprietor	Pennsylvania

1. Identifying What is the title of the table?

_____

2. Defining What are the features of a charter colony?

_____

3. Classifying What kind of colony is Pennsylvania?

_____

_____

Social Studies Skills Activity (continued)

✓ Applying the Skill

Directions: Complete the following table with the choices provided below about the early American colonies. Use your textbook to help you place the information.

Delaware	Connecticut	Georgia
Royal	elected their governor	appointed the governor
ruled directly by British		

Different Kinds of Early American Colonies		
Type	**Features**	**Example**
Charter	rights and privileges granted by British monarchy to stockholders _____	Rhode Island _____
Proprietary _____	owned by individual proprietor _____ _____	Pennsylvania _____

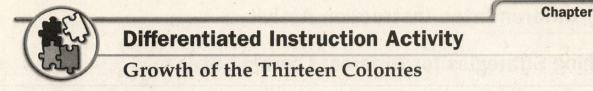

Differentiated Instruction Activity

Growth of the Thirteen Colonies

The New England Primer

The New England Primer was a small textbook first published in Boston in about 1683. Most of the children of colonial America learned to read from this book. The *Primer* included rhymed couplets to teach the alphabet, vocabulary words, and numerous short poems and reading selections. Three typical excerpts are provided below.

Good Children must,

Fear God all Day,	Love Christ alway,	Awake, arise, behold thou hast
Parents obey,	In Secret Pray,	Thy Life a Leaf, thy Breath a Blast;
No false thing say,	Mind little Play,	At Night lye down prepar'd to have
By no Sin stray,	Make no delay,	Thy sleep, thy death, thy bed, thy grave.
	In doing Good.	

A. In Adam's Fall, We Sinned all.

B. Thy Life to Mend, This Book Attend.

C. The Cat doth play, And after slay.

D. A Dog will bite, A Thief at night.

E. An Eagle's flight, Is out of sight.

F. The Idle Fool, Is whipt at School.

G. As runs the Glass, Man's life doth pass.

H. My Book and Heart, Shall never part.

J. Job feels the Rod, Yet blesses God.

K. Our KING the good, No man of blood.

L. The Lion bold, The Lamb doth hold.

M. The Moon gives light, In time of night.

N. Nightingales sing, In Time of Spring.

O. The Royal Oak it was the tree, That sav'd his Royal Majestie.

P. Peter denies, His Lord and cries.

Q. Queen Esther comes in Royal State, To save the JEWS from dismal Fate.

R. Rachel doth mourn, For her first born.

S. Samuel anoints, Whom God appoints.

T. Time cuts down all, Both great and small.

U. Uriah's beauteous Wife, Made David seek his Life.

X. Xerxes the great did die, And so must you & I.

Y. Youth forward slips, Death soonest nips.

Z. Zaccheus he did climb the tree, His Lord to see.

Source: *The New England Primer*, 1727 edition. Reproduced in *Anthology of American Literature: Colonial Through Romantic*. New York: Macmillan, 1980.

Directions: Use the information from the excerpts and your textbook to answer the following questions on a separate sheet of paper.

1. Identifying What is the source for most of the references given in the alphabet lesson?

2. Drawing Conclusions Do you think the values communicated in the *Primer* were representative of colonial America in general? Why or why not?

Differentiated Instruction Activity (continued)

Teaching Strategies for Different Learning Styles

The following activities are ways the basic lesson can be modified to accommodate students' different learning styles.

English Language Learner (EL)

Have students identify differences between contemporary English spelling, capitalization, and punctuation and those shown in the *Primer* excerpts.

Gifted and Talented

The New England Primer was the most widely used schoolbook of early America. More than 5 million copies are reported to have been published and used. Ask students to write a three-page paper (1) speculating about the effect of the *Primer* on the colonial American mind, and (2) discussing any influences they see persisting today.

Verbal/Linguistic

Students can concisely represent many ideas by brainstorming and using one-sentence summaries. Brainstorm with students on a large sheet of flip chart paper the qualities and characteristics about Puritans and Puritanism. After 3 to 5 minutes, ask the students to write a one-sentence summary of the list, in 25 words or less, based on the following model: *A Puritan was a person who....*

Logical/Mathematical

Venn diagrams help students categorize and classify information by comparing and/or contrasting multiple items. Advise students that they will need a simple children's ABC book for this activity. Have students draw a Venn diagram. They should title one circle "New England Primer"; the other should have the title of the book they are using. Students should then study both alphabet lessons, writing information about each in the respective circle. Qualities that both lessons share fit into the overlapping area between the two circles.

Auditory/Musical

Have students create a song that could be used to help young children memorize the alphabet. Allow students to perform their songs in class. Discuss the different approaches taken by students.

Interpersonal

Organize students into pairs. Have each pair brainstorm traits that they believe all "good children" should have today. Then have the pair collaborate on a short poem that teaches their ideas, using the example from the *Primer* as a guide. Discuss students' poems in class.

Intrapersonal

Ask students to prepare a two-page paper that (1) identifies at least two cultural values that are reflected in the excerpts from the *Primer,* and (2) determines the cultural values reflected in the textbooks they are now using.

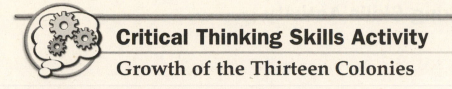

Critical Thinking Skills Activity

Growth of the Thirteen Colonies

Distinguishing Fact from Opinion

✔ Learning the Skill

A fact is a statement that can be proved. An opinion is a personal belief that cannot be proved. For example:

Fact: France and England established colonies in North America in the 1600s.

Opinion: The English enjoyed frontier life more than the French did.

When you analyze a book, a newspaper, or a magazine article to distinguish fact from opinion, check for statements that you can verify. Statements that contain certain words or phrases, such as *should*, *the most important*, or *the most interesting*, are often used when stating an opinion.

✔ Practicing the Skill

Directions: Read the following passage. Identify each numbered sentence as either fact (F) or opinion (O). Give a reason for each choice.

The Middle Colonies

(1) The Middle Colonies were located between New England and the colonies of the South. (2) They were the most important colonies in English America. (3) The Middle Colonies enjoyed fertile soil and a slightly milder climate than that of New England. Farmers in this region cultivated larger tracts of land and produced bigger harvests than those in New England. (4) The New England farmers were not as industrious as the farmers in the Middle Colonies. (5) In New York and Pennsylvania, farmers grew large quantities of wheat and other cash crops. (6) Crops grown in the Middle Colonies tasted better than those grown in New England. (7) Farmers also sent cargoes of wheat and livestock to New York City and Philadelphia for shipment. (8) This commerce helped these cities become busy ports.

1. _____

   _____

2. _____

   _____

3. _____

   _____

Critical Thinking Skills Activity (continued)

4. _____

_____

5. _____

_____

6. _____

_____

7. _____

_____

8. _____

_____

✓ Applying the Skill

Directions: In the blank at the left, write the letter of the choice that best answers the question.

_____ 1. Which of following statements is a fact?

   A. All Native Americans disliked European settlers.

   B. Native Americans had to side with the French during the French and Indian War.

   C. British General Edward Braddock should not have been sent on a mission in the American wilderness.

   D. During the early stages of the French and Indian War, the Americans got little help from England.

_____ 2. Which of the following statements is an opinion?

   A. George Washington was a surveyor as a young man.

   B. Washington was the best soldier in the English colonies.

   C. The governor of Virginia made Washington a lieutenant colonel and sent him to the Ohio country before the French and Indian War.

   D. Washington's fame spread when accounts of his experience in the Ohio country were published.

Geography and History Activity

Growth of the Thirteen Colonies

Making a Living

How were the people in the new thirteen colonies—from the rocky coast of New England to the low-lying plains of the South—going to remain unified and survive? Some outside observers did not think it was possible.

New England Resourcefulness

The colonies, however, continued to grow. Immigration from Europe and Africa was one reason, and the land itself was another. Farming became an important means of survival for everyone, even in New England, where the thin, rocky soil permitted colonists to grow only enough good for their own families. But New Englanders became resourceful. Some started small businesses to make ends meet, such as making and selling soap.

New Englanders also used wood from the abundant forests in the region to create large shipbuilding and fishing industries. Ships from New England sailed south along the coast, allowing the colonies to trade with each other. Now the colonies were economically interdependent.

Shipping and Trade

These ships also set up key trade routes to Europe, the Caribbean, and Africa, bringing needed supplies to all of the colonies. The bustling cities of New York and Philadelphia became major ports in the shipping trade. Farmers in this region benefited from the milder climate and more fertile soil. They produced larger crops, such as wheat, that they could sell in the colonies and overseas. People in the Middle Colonies also engaged in mining, lumbering, and manufacturing.

Down South

The South had the richest soil and warmest climate. Most settlers in these colonies made their living from farming. In Maryland and Virginia, many planters became rich from growing tobacco, particularly if they owned large properties. In South Carolina and Georgia—in low-lying areas along the coast—planting rice was even more profitable. The labor required to harvest both tobacco and rice, however, was enormous. Many growers were willing to import and use Africans as slave labor—and even hired bosses to make sure their slaves worked hard. The economies in these states grew faster than anywhere else in the colonies.

Settlers in the thirteen colonies learned to work together to survive in their new homelands. The use of slave labor, however, would one day destroy their solidarity.

Geography and History Activity (continued)

Directions: Answer the following questions on the map or in the spaces provided. You may abbreviate if you wish.

1. **Specifying** Color each of the colonial regions with a different color. Then label each region.

2. **Labeling** Dots on the map show the locations of the four most important colonial seaports: Boston, New York City, Charles Town, and Philadelphia. Label each city.

3. **Locating** In the correct location write the name of each of the following colonies: Pennsylvania, North Carolina, Massachusetts, Virginia, Georgia, and New York.

4. **Determining Cause and Effect** What effect did the geography of New England have on its economy?

_____

_____

5. **Predicting** What might have happened to the economy of the Southern Colonies if Africans had not been imported as slaves?

_____

_____

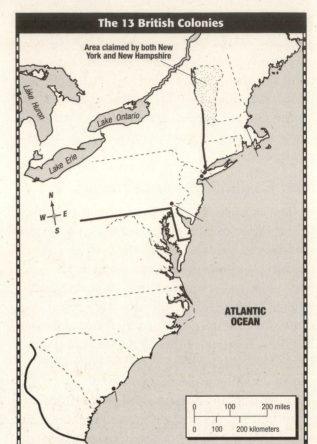

GOING FURTHER ▶ ▶▶▶

- Large numbers of Germans settled in Pennsylvania during the Colonial era. Many became successful farmers using methods they had learned in Europe. Dutch, Swedish, and other Europeans also settled in the Middle Colonies during this time. Research one of these groups and describe how their communities and lifestyles differed from those of other settlers in their regions. Write a descriptive report about your findings.

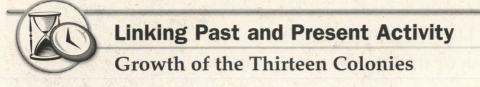

Linking Past and Present Activity

Growth of the Thirteen Colonies

The Printing Press

THEN The first printing press in the English colonies was set up in 1639. Printers arranged type—movable letters made of metal—on a platform. The printer spread ink over the type and placed a sheet of paper on top. The platform was positioned under a plate connected to a large screw. When the printer turned a screw by a lever, an impression was printed onto the paper.

The printing press helped spread new political ideas. Newspapers made it possible for colonists to learn about events and ideas in other colonies. In January 1776 Thomas Paine published a pamphlet called *Common Sense*. In it he urged immediate separation from Britain. More than 150,000 copies of the pamphlet were sold in the thirteen colonies. *Common Sense* influenced public opinion toward independence.

Screw

Lever

Paper holder

Type tray

Printing Press

NOW More than 200 years later, printing still plays a major role in spreading ideas. Some printing methods have changed, however. Today type is set by computer instead of by hand. Most printing does not use movable type at all; instead, a photographic impression of an entire page is designed in a computer and transferred to a plate, and then the plate is applied to paper.

Transmission technology makes it possible to send news quickly over tremendous distances. Magazines such as *Newsweek*, *TIME*, and *U.S. News & World Report* transmit their information by satellite to printing locations around the country. As information becomes available on the Internet, some printing functions don't take place on printing presses at all. Instead, information is printed in homes on computer printers.

Making a Front Page   DIRECTIONS: If you could have the front page of your own newspaper published and distributed across the country, what would you want it to look like? Front pages try to grab attention with headlines and photographs. Collect several local and national newspapers and bring them to class. What stories are on the front pages? What current events do the national papers cover? How do the local newspapers differ? Create a front page to a national newspaper using events from the French and Indian War. Use the library to find more details about the war.

Time Line Activity

Growth of the Thirteen Colonies

Wars Between Britain and France in America

Directions: Use your textbook and the information in the time line to answer the questions in the spaces provided.

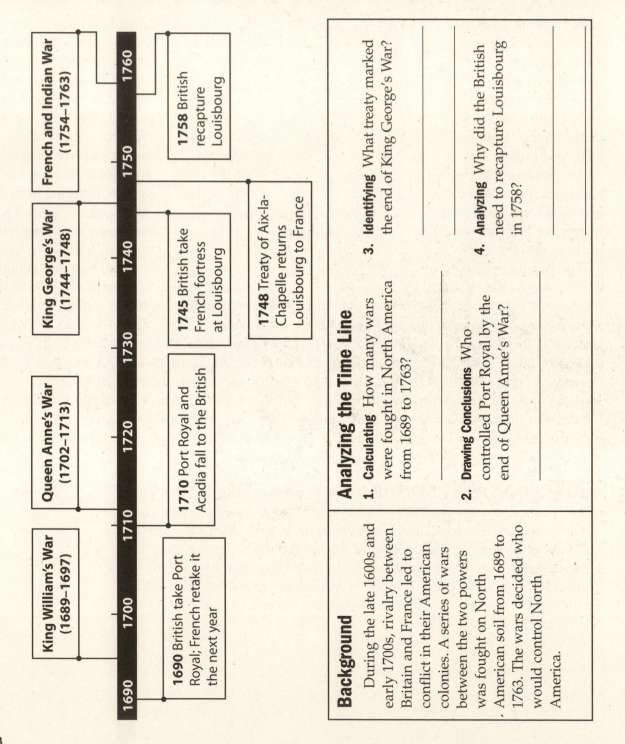

King William's War (1689–1697)

1690 British take Port Royal; French retake it the next year

Queen Anne's War (1702–1713)

1710 Port Royal and Acadia fall to the British

King George's War (1744–1748)

1745 British take French fortress at Louisbourg

1748 Treaty of Aix-la-Chapelle returns Louisbourg to France

French and Indian War (1754–1763)

1758 British recapture Louisbourg

1690 1700 1710 1720 1730 1740 1750 1760

Background

During the late 1600s and early 1700s, rivalry between Britain and France led to conflict in their American colonies. A series of wars between the two powers was fought on North American soil from 1689 to 1763. The wars decided who would control North America.

Analyzing the Time Line

1. **Calculating** How many wars were fought in North America from 1689 to 1763?

2. **Drawing Conclusions** Who controlled Port Royal by the end of Queen Anne's War?

3. **Identifying** What treaty marked the end of King George's War?

4. **Analyzing** Why did the British need to recapture Louisbourg in 1758?

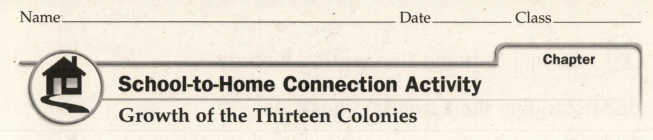

School-to-Home Connection Activity

Growth of the Thirteen Colonies

Chapter

What Do You Know?

Directions: Ask each other the following questions to see how much you know about Growth of the Thirteen Colonies.*

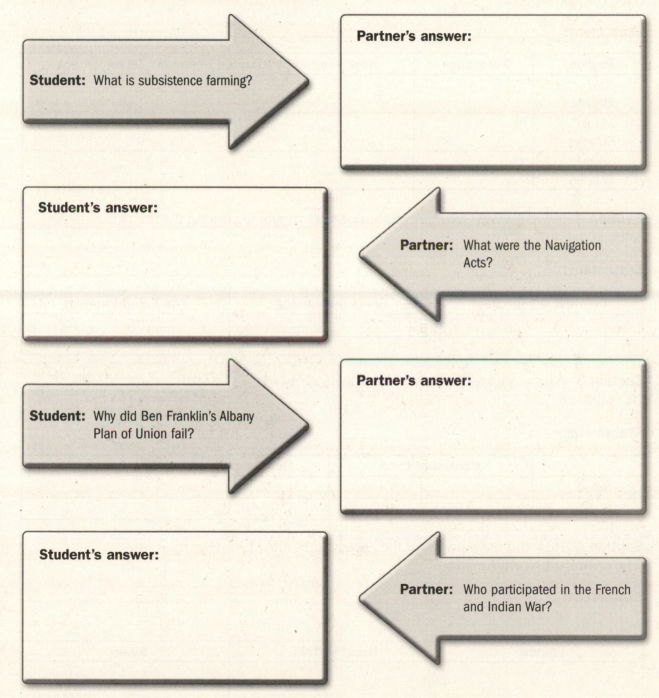

Student: What is subsistence farming?

Partner's answer:

Student's answer:

Partner: What were the Navigation Acts?

Student: Why did Ben Franklin's Albany Plan of Union fail?

Partner's answer:

Student's answer:

Partner: Who participated in the French and Indian War?

*With your student, find answers to these questions in the student textbook.

🏠 School-to-Home Connection Activity (continued)

Understanding the Essential Questions

Directions: Rewrite each Essential Question as a statement. Then fill in the table below the statement.

Section 1 How did geography affect the economic development of the three colonial regions?

Statement: _____

Region	Geography	How Geography Affected Economic Development
New England		
Middle Colonies		
Southern Colonies		

Section 2 In what ways was an American culture developing during the colonial period?

Statement: _____

Colonial Government	Great Awakening	The Enlightenment

Section 3 Why was there conflict in North America between France and Great Britain?

Statement: _____

	Control of Land	Relationship with Native Americans
British		
French		

Section 4 How did the outcome of the French and Indian War determine who controlled North America?

Statement: _____

France	Great Britain	Spain

Reteaching Activity

Growth of the Thirteen Colonies

Between 1607 and 1770, the American colonies developed into unique regions. Each region had different characteristics. The climate, type of soil, and natural resources influenced how the settlers made their living.

Comparing and Contrasting **DIRECTIONS:** Read each statement in the list below. Decide whether the statement describes the New England Colonies, the Middle Colonies, or the Southern Colonies. Some statements describe two regions or all three regions. Write the letter of each statement in the appropriate section of the Venn diagram.

A. long winters and thin, rocky soil

B. little industry

C. cultural diversity due to many German, Dutch, and Swedish immigrants

D. well-organized towns with central meetinghouse

E. plantations and slave labor

F. growing population

G. experienced the Great Awakening

H. subsistence farming

I. had schools run by Quakers

J. farming main economic activity

K. fishing and shipbuilding important economic activities

L. main cash crops were tobacco and rice

M. climate and soil suited to cash crops

N. coastal cities became center of shipping trade

O. included the two largest cities in the colonies by the 1760s

P. supported the British in the French and Indian War

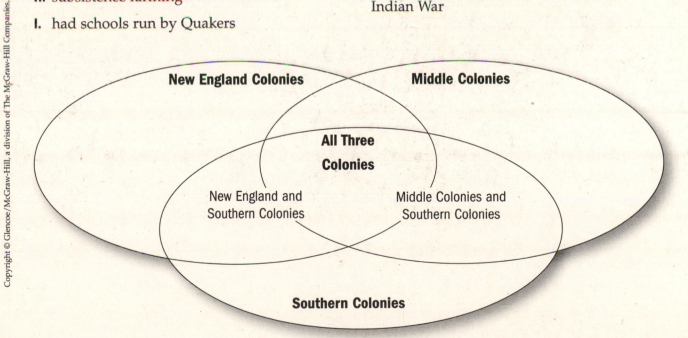

Section Resources

Guided Reading Activity

Growth of the Thirteen Colonies

Life in the Colonies

Reading Tip After reading the section, list aspects of life in the different colonies. Then go back and check to make sure what you've written is correct.

Answering Questions **DIRECTIONS:** As you read the section, answer the questions below.

1. **Defining** What is subsistence farming?

_____

_____

2. **Analyzing** Why was shipbuilding able to become an important industry in the New England Colonies?

_____

_____

3. **Identifying** What was the name given to the section of the triangular trade route where enslaved Africans were shipped to the West Indies?

_____

4. **Naming** Which cities in the Middle Colonies became busy ports?

_____

5. **Listing** What were some of the industries of the Middle Colonies?

_____

6. **Differentiating** What were the main cash crops in Maryland, Virginia, South Carolina, and Georgia?

_____

_____

7. **Defining** What were slave codes?

_____

Guided Reading Activity

Growth of the Thirteen Colonies

Government, Religion, Culture

Reading Tip   Read for the purpose of understanding the material, not just to answer the questions below.

Reading for Accuracy   DIRECTIONS: Use your textbook to decide if a statement is true or false. Write **T** or **F** in the blank. If a statement is false, rewrite it to make it true.

_____ **1.** William and Mary signed an American Bill of Rights guaranteeing certain basic rights to all colonists.

_____

_____ **2.** To make money from its trade, England had to import more goods than it exported.

_____

_____ **3.** The Navigation Acts directed the trade between England and the colonies.

_____

_____ **4.** The Magna Carta established the principle of unlimited government.

_____

_____ **5.** Colonists in charter colonies elected their governors and members of the legislature.

_____

_____ **6.** In proprietary colonies, the members of the lower house of the legislature were appointed by the proprietors.

_____

_____ **7.** Under colonial legislature, most women, indentured servants, landless poor, and African Americans could not vote.

_____

_____ **8.** In colonial society, men were the formal heads of the households and represented the family in the community.

_____

Section

Guided Reading Activity

Growth of the Thirteen Colonies

France and Britain Clash

Reading Tip When the reading becomes difficult, slow down and reread that paragraph. If you still do not understand the text, highlight it and ask your teacher for help.

Filling in the Blanks DIRECTIONS: Use your textbook to fill in the blanks using the words in the box. Use another sheet of paper if necessary.

balance of power	Iroquois Confederacy	missionaries
Native American	British	militia
colony	French	George Washington
land	French and Indian War	New York
defeat	Albany Plan of Union	Ohio

A rivalry existed between the British and **(1)** _____ colonists in North America. The French had many **(2)** _____ allies because they did not want to take over their **(3)** _____ and because French **(4)** _____ converted many of them to Catholicism.

The **(5)** _____ in the East remained independent by trading with both the British and the French, but eventually became allies of the **(6)** _____. This upset the **(7)** _____ between the British and French.

(8) _____ was sent into **(9)** _____ country to demand that the British leave, but they refused. He was sent back with a **(10)** _____ to build a fort. They attacked a French force, but this ended in **(11)** _____.

Representatives from several colonies met in **(12)** _____ to discuss the threat of war. They adopted the **(13)** _____ for a united government. However, no **(14)** _____ was willing to give up any of its power. Soon after, the **(15)** _____ erupted.

Section

Guided Reading Activity

Growth of the Thirteen Colonies

The French and Indian War

Reading Tip Concentrate while you read. Read alone in a quiet room with the television and radio turned off.

Outlining DIRECTIONS: Reading the section and completing the outline below will help you learn more about the French and Indian War. Refer to your textbook to fill in the blanks.

I. The British Take Action

   A. The French network of _____ with Native Americans allowed them to control large areas of land.

   B. General Edward Braddock was appointed to drive the French out of the _____ , but he failed because the British army's bright-colored _____ and marching _____ in formation made them easy targets.

   C. The fighting in America helped start the _____ _____ in Europe.

   D. _____ decided that Great Britain would pay for the war supplies, no matter their cost.

II. The Fall of New France

   A. Britain's greatest victory occurred in the _____.

   B. The _____ forced France to give Canada and most of it lands east of the _____ to Great Britain.

III. Trouble on the Frontier

   A. Native Americans killed settlers along the Pennsylvania and Virginia frontiers during _____.

   B. The Proclamation of 1763 set the _____ as the temporary western boundary of the colonies.

Answer Key

The Americas: Worlds Meet

Citizenship and Decision-Making Activity

Questions to Consider

1. Answers may vary but may mention the desire for wealth and power or status in European society.

2. Entrepreneurs provide products or services to fill a need. They provide job opportunities. Students may mention that entrepreneurs are partly responsible for our high standard of living in the United States.

3. Student responses will vary but could include such entrepreneurs as Bill Gates, Donald Trump, Mary Kay, or Ted Turner.

Your Task

Check students' Self-Assessment Checklists. Students should complete the Citizenship and Decision-Making Activity by working individually or in a group as directed in the How to Do It section. At the end of the project, have students review their work by discussing difficulties they may have faced during the project and how they resolved those difficulties. Encourage students to explain how they would improve their work if they did this project again.

Economics and History Activity

Applying Economics to History

1. Answers will vary. Students should note that white colonists probably did not see enslaved Africans as "people." Most treated enslaved people like property. Also, colonists had an economic reason to deny the right of freedom to enslaved people. They were a source of cheap labor for growing the crops that were in high demand.

2. The importation of enslaved Africans greatly increased until it dropped by half after Congress outlawed the slave trade.

3. Cotton exports increased greatly, doubling from 1800 to 1820.

4. The importation of enslaved Africans was cut by over half, but it was not stopped entirely.

5. Answers will vary but should show an understanding that the Southern economy was directly dependent on enslaved labor as a plentiful and profitable labor force.

Going Further With Economics

Students' paragraphs should indicate that the cotton gin was invented in 1793. The effects of this invention are reflected in the graphs by the dramatic increase in exportation of cotton and the increase in importation of enslaved Africans after 1793.

Reading Skills Activity

Practicing the Skill

Main Idea:
New England was the center of the shipping trade in America.

↓

Supporting Idea:
New England linked the English American colonies to one another and to different parts of the world.

↓

Supporting Idea:
Some ships followed trade routes.

↓

Ships brought sugar and molasses from the West Indies to New England colonies.	*Sugar and molasses were made into rum and shipped to West Africa and traded for enslaved Africans.*	*Enslaved Africans were take to the West Indies and traded to planters.*

Answer Key

Applying the Skill

> **Main idea:**
> The Great Awakening was an important religious movement that swept through the colonies from the 1720s through the 1740s.

↓

> **Supporting idea:**
> Revivalist preachers such as Jonathan Edwards and George Whitefield attracted large, appreciative crowds.

↓

> **Supporting idea:**
> The Great Awakening increased church membership and strengthened the faith of many colonists.

↓

> **Supporting idea:**
> The Great Awakening helped affirm ideals of independent thought and religious freedom.

American Literature Reading

1. Virtue
2. Because wisdom was higher than fools could reach—Wheatley believed she was not wise enough to fully understand Virtue.
3. She need not despair because even though she could not fully understand Virtue, Virtue hovered about her, guiding her and teaching her and leading her toward endless life and bliss.
4. Virtue would embrace her, help her be pure, help her resist false joys, and guide her to endless life (she would live on after death) and bliss.

Interpreting Political Cartoons

1. The letters stand for the colonies and colonial groupings.
2. The New England colonies are grouped together under the label "N.E." and Georgia is not included.
3. In unity there is strength. (a.)

4. The message was that the colonies could not survive unless they collaborated more closely.
5. Answers will vary. On the affirmative side, national unity is important in an age of racial discord. On the negative side, the idea of a strong national government is overwhelmingly accepted by Americans today, and the relevancy of Franklin's message is not needed because it is generally accepted.
6. Answers will vary, but students should include the concept that there is strength in unity.
7. Answers will vary, but the discussion of symbolism will give the students a better insight into the mind of a cartoonist.

The First Americans

Content Vocabulary Activity

1. carbon dating
2. nomad
3. theocracy
4. archaeology
5. clan
6. Quechua
7. artifact
8. pueblo
9. hieroglyphics
10. migration
11. civilization
12. quipus
13. maize
14. federation
15. terrace
16. culture

Academic Vocabulary Activity

A. Word Meaning

1. point of origin
2. measurement
3. sophisticated
4. connect
5. building
6. civilization

B. Word Usage

1. linked
2. structures
3. estimates or estimations
4. complex
5. cultures
6. sources

Answer Key

C. Word Family

1. verb
2. noun, verb, adjective
3. verb, adjective
4. noun, verb
5. verb, adjective
6. adjective
7. noun, verb
8. noun
9. verb
10. noun, verb
11. noun
12. adjective
13. verb, adjective

Primary Source Readings

1. The Mayan chant and Aztec song predict that an invader will destroy their way of life.
2. Possible words include dust, darken, blight, wither, cloud, seize, ruin, destroyed, death, hanging dead, battle, scattered, sad, mournful, afflicted, broken, disarray, struggled
3. Answers will vary according to students' responses.
4. The general message of the chant and song predicts that, even though their societies are strong, the Maya and Aztec civilizations will collapse under the power of a stronger enemy.
5. Prophecies could include topics such as terrorist threats, global warming, or references drawn from sacred scriptures.

Writing Skills Activity

Practicing the Skill

1. There are several theories as to who the Mound Builders were.
2. The population of Mississippian societies declined for several reasons.

3. Mounds can have different shapes and purposes.

Applying the Skill

Check students' self-assessment checklists. Students' paragraphs should contain a topic sentence and at least two supporting sentences. The topic sentence should make a clear point and be general enough to allow for elaboration. Each supporting sentence should relate to the main idea of the paragraph and provide supporting details. Some students may provide paragraphs with related sentences but which have no clear main idea. Help these students write a clear topic sentence by explaining what the details they have written are about.

Social Studies Skills Activity

Practicing the Skill

1. The time line shows when cultures arose in the Americas and when Europeans arrived.
2. The time span is c. 28,000–13,000 B.C. The time intervals are random until 1100. From 1100 forward there are 100-year intervals.
3. The migration was from Asia across Beringia.
4. The drought struck in c. 1130.

Applying the Skill

1. The missing interval is 1400.
2. The four items should be added to the time line in the appropriate boxes.
3. The time span is 1215 to 1400. The time intervals are 100 years.
4. Thirteen years—Mali in A.D. 1312 and Tenochtitlán in A.D. 1325.

Differentiated Instruction Activity

1. Tools and objects used by both cultures include roads, bridges, freeze-dried foods, beautiful textile and metalwork,

Answer Key

a complex series of irrigation canals and aqueducts, and a wide array of musical instruments.

2. Students' answers will vary. Possible answer: The Inca's stonework did the most to preserve their history, since archaeologists can learn much about the culture by studying the ruins. The extensive road system helped spread the Inca Empire by making travel easier. The method of terrace farming did the most to feed the Inca by increasing the amount of arable land.

Critical Thinking Skills Activity

Practicing the Skill

1. It shows the Native American population density in different parts of North America.
2. Central America, southern Mexico, and the Caribbean
3. the northern part of North America and certain patches in the central part of the continent

Applying the Skill

1. B   2. A

Geography and History Activity

1. Check students' maps.
2, 3, 4. Possible answers:

Region	Foods	Housing	Characteristic
Northwest Coast	salmon	wooden houses	(4) used resources of the forest and sea
Far North	caribou	igloos	(3) clothing made from fur and seal-skins
California Intermountain	small game, berries	shelters made of branches and reeds	(5) nomadic
Southwest	buffalo meat, maize	adobe houses, pueblos, and hogans	(6) Apache and Navajo
Great Plains	buffalo meat	tepees	(1) used horses in warfare
Eastern Woodlands	corn, nuts	wooden houses	(2) created a government
Southeast	corn, squash	wooden houses	(7) famed river bottomlands

5. There were many different groups of early Native Americans and they lived in many different regions on the continent. They all learned how to adapt to the region they settled in.

Linking Past and Present Activity

1. Native Americans planted more than one field in the hopes that at least one would flourish. They planted in dried-up river-beds to ensure moisture in the ground.
2. They boiled the sap down or let it evaporate to produce sugar.
3. Corn is used as food for both humans and animals. It is also an important energy source.
4. Native Americans used hand tools to tap trees and containers to collect the sap. Today, the tapping is mechanized, and the sap runs through tubing to evaporation stations.
5. Answers will vary, but since Native Americans often used wood fires to cook their food and to provide warmth, they may have seen sweet sap running out of the ends of logs they cut and burned.

Answer Key

Time Line Activity

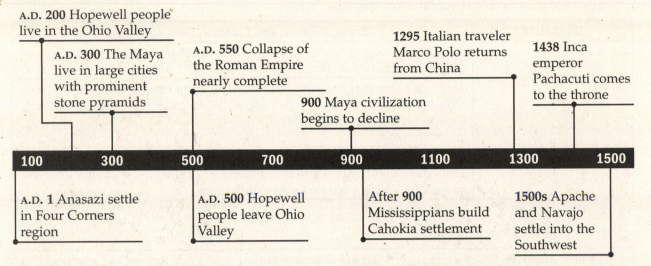

A.D. 200 Hopewell people live in the Ohio Valley

A.D. 300 The Maya live in large cities with prominent stone pyramids

A.D. 550 Collapse of the Roman Empire nearly complete

900 Maya civilization begins to decline

1295 Italian traveler Marco Polo returns from China

1438 Inca emperor Pachacuti comes to the throne

| 100 | 300 | 500 | 700 | 900 | 1100 | 1300 | 1500 |

A.D. 1 Anasazi settle in Four Corners region

A.D. 500 Hopewell people leave Ohio Valley

After 900 Mississippians build Cahokia settlement

1500s Apache and Navajo settle into the Southwest

School-to-Home Connection Activity

What Do You Know?

Sample answers:

Partner's answer: Beringia is a land bridge that ran from Siberia to Alaska.

Student's answer: Maya priests developed a 365-day calendar

Partner's answer: The Inca people cut terraces into the mountain slopes and built stone walls to keep the soil and plants on the terraces.

Student's answer: The Adena were early Mound Builders who lived around 800 B.C. in what is now the Ohio Valley.

Understanding the Essential Questions

Sample answers:

1. Statement: Agriculture changed the lives of the early people.

Before Agriculture	After Agriculture
Early people relied on hunting for much of their food. Hunting does not provide a stable food supply for large groups of people.	Early people had a more reliable food supply and more people could be fed.
Early people were nomads because they had to follow the herds they hunted.	Early people could stay in one place. This allowed them to build permanent homes and villages, and spend time on other activities.
Early people could not carry much with them.	Staying in one place meant that early people could create and keep more things.

Answer Key

2. Statement: The early civilizations of Mexico and Central America developed socially, politically, and economically.

Civilization	Social, Political, and Economic Developments
Olmec	developed strong agriculture, sculpted monuments, built cities, stone pavement, and drainage systems
Maya	developed strong agriculture; built huge pyramids and large cities; had a complex religion and society; developed 365-day calendar; demonstrated knowledge in astronomy and mathematics; created written language; participated in trade
Aztec	built one of the greatest and largest cities in the Americas; used engineering methods to build causeways; became center of trade; had a complex society and religion; built huge towers and buildings

3. Statement: The way of life of Native Americans in North America was related to their environments.

Native American Group	Type of Environment	Adaptations to Environment
Hohokam	hot and dry	dug irrigation channels to water their fields
Inuit (North)	cold Arctic climate	lived in igloos; hunted on land and sea; made warm, waterproof clothing from furs
Tlingit, Haida, Chinook (Northwest)	moderate climate near forest and sea	lived in wooden houses, made things from tree bark, fished for food
People of the Plains	wide open, grassy plains	nomadic; hunted large herds for food; learned to tame and ride horses for hunting and fighting; had small, temporary vegetable plots
Creek, Chickasaw, Cherokee (Southeast)	woodlands, warm climate	farmed for food in fertile soil

Reteaching Activity

1. 5, A
2. 6, F
3. 2, E
4. 7, C
5. 4, B

Guided Reading Activity

Migration to the Americas

1. Artifacts are the tools, weapons, baskets, and carvings of early peoples.

2. Archaeologists believe the first peoples came to the Americas across a land bridge that connected Asia and the Americas.

3. The name of the land bridge is Beringia.

4. The most recent Ice Age began 100,000 years ago and ended about 12,000 years ago.

5. People who move from place to place are called nomads.

6. Early Americans hunted the mammoth and used its meat for food, skin for clothing, bones for weapons and tools, and possibly its ribs to build shelters.

7. Mammoths and other large animals began to die out, which forced the early Americans to look for other sources of food.

Answer Key

8. Farming provided a reliable source of food, so people no longer had to move from place to place. It also allowed people to spend time on activities other than finding food.

9. Carbon dating is a method of estimating the age of an artifact.

Cities and Empires

I. **A.** 1500 B.C., 300 B.C.
   B. temple
      1. theocracy
      2. hieroglyphics
      3. jungle, Mexico's
   C. Mexico
      1. Tenochititlán
      2. military
      3. human sacrifices
II. **A.** largest
   B. war
   C. Quechua

North American Peoples

1. T.
2. F. The Anasazi lived in pueblos and cliff dwellings.
3. F. Among the earliest Mound Builders were the Adena, who were hunters and gatherers.
4. T.
5. F. Salmon was important to the Tlingit, Nez Perce, and Yakima.
6. F. The Hopi, Acoma, and Zuni in the Southwest built adobe homes and raised corn as their basic food.
7. T.
8. F. Members of the Iroquois League were organized according to clans.
9. T.

Exploring the Americas

Content Vocabulary Activity

1. Quran
2. saga
3. Columbian Exchange
4. conquistador
5. mosque
6. line of demarcation
7. mercantilism
8. classical
9. astrolabe
10. coureur de bois
11. pueblo
12. strait
13. pilgrimage
14. encomienda
15. Northwest Passage
16. plantation
17. technology
18. circumnavigate
19. mission

Academic Vocabulary Activity

A. Word Meaning

1. D
2. H
3. B
4. F
5. A
6. C
7. E
8. G

B. Word Usage

1. c
2. d
3. f
4. a
5. e
6. b

Primary Source Readings

1. The Aztec gods give the people health, water, good seedtimes and weather, and victories.

Answer Key

2. The god Uichilobos was the god of war. The god Texcatepuca was the god of hell and was in charge of the souls of the Mexicans. The god that was half man and half lizard was in charge of the sowing and ripening.

3. Cortés characterizes the Aztec gods as evil things or devils.

4. The Aztecs must worship and sacrifice to their gods.

5. The important god of war is decorated with precious stones and gold and is circled by snakes and carries a bow and arrows to represent war. His brother the god of hell has the face of a bear to frighten the people and also is covered with gold and precious stones. The god of sowing and ripening, half man and half lizard, is said to be filled with all the seeds there are in the world, which would help the people to grow food.

Writing Skills Activity

Practicing the Skill
1. (a) This sentence presents a general statement that explains what the other sentences are about.

2. (b) This sentence does not relate to the main idea, which is about how disease played a role in the Spanish conquest.

3. (c) and (d) These sentences expand on the main idea with details of how disease played a role in the Spanish conquest of the Americas.

Applying the Skill
Answers will vary but should describe the technology and give details about how it affected exploration. Sample answers:
1. Mapmakers were able to make more accurate land and sea maps through the use of information from explorers' reports and Arab geographers. These maps charted parts of the world beyond Europe. They included the direction of ocean currents and lines of latitude.

2. Better instruments were developed for navigating the seas. Sailors could use an astrolabe, which measures the position of the stars, to determine their latitude. They also used the compass to determine their location when they were far from land.

3. Advances in ship design allowed shipbuilders to build sailing vessels capable of long ocean voyages. The three-masted caravel, developed by the Portuguese, sailed faster and carried more cargo and food supplies than earlier ships. It also could float in shallow water, which allowed sailors to explore inlets and sail their ships up to the beach to make repairs.

Social Studies Skills Activity

Practicing the Skill
1. The key is located in the upper left corner.

2. The scale is shown in miles and kilometers.

3. Taos is the northernmost pueblo.

4. It is approximately 60 miles from Albuquerque to Santa Fe.

Applying the Skill
1. Students should draw the indicated points of interest as well as the parts of a map.

2. Students should draw a path between the two points of interest, noting the miles between them.

3. Students should use their compass rose in order to answer the question.

4. Students should use the distances on their maps to answer the questions.

Differentiated Instruction Activity
1. Students' time lines may vary but should reflect the information found in the excerpt in correct sequence.

Answer Key

2. During the Middle Ages, European maps were inaccurate representations of the world based on religious beliefs. Arabic maps were very accurate and based on more scientific principles.

Critical Thinking Skills Activity

Practicing the Skill
1. **Cause:** Wealthy Europeans wanted spices and other goods from Asia. **Effect:** Italian merchants bought the goods from Arab traders in the Middle East and sent them to European ports.
2. **Cause:** Better ships, maps, and navigation tools developed during the 1400s. **Effect:** There were longer ocean voyages by the mid-1400s.
3. **Cause:** Spain wanted to participate in the rich trade with Asia. **Effect:** Spain financed Columbus's attempts to find a route to Asia by sailing westward across the Atlantic.

Applying the Skill
1. A
2. C
3. B
4. A

Geography and History Activity

1. People's perceptions of regions are influenced by their experiences, by the knowledge they have about a land and its people, and by political motivations or restrictions.
2. Spanish: mineral wealth—gold and silver; French: furs; English: rich land for farming
3. Discovering the mild climate and rich soil in Virginia, the English were eager to set up agricultural colonies that could supply the homeland with food.
4. Since the French traders were interested in the fur trade, they lived a nomadic life similar to the Native Americans. The English were more interested in farming. They established well-defined communities.

5. The English, French, and Spanish all had different ideas about what fortunes they would find in North America, and this affected how they explored and colonized the continent.

Linking Past and Present Activity

1. Charts will vary, but should show the price of gold for three weeks, the amount of daily increase or decrease, and the percentage change. Students should use their charts to support their answers to the questions.
2. Posters will vary, but should include the price of one ounce (28 g) of gold, and show groceries that could be purchased for that price.

Time Line Activity

1. Columbus made four voyages.
2. Cortés invaded Mexico.
3. Ponce de León
4. Pizarro conquered the Inca.

School-to-Home Connection Activity

What Do You Know?

Sample answers:

Partner's answer: The Renaissance was a period of intellectual and artistic creativity. It began in the 1300s.

Student's answer: Portuguese explorer Vasco da Gama, guided by an Arab pilot, first sailed the eastern sea route from Europe to Asia.

Partner's answer: Juan Ponce de León was hunting for the fountain of youth.

Student's answer: Explorers wanted to find a direct water route through the Americas to shorten the journey from Europe to Asia.

Answer Key

Understanding the Essential Questions

Sample answers:

1. Statement: Several events and technological advances paved the way for European exploration.

People became interested in exploring when they heard about the Crusades and Marco Polo's trips to Asia.	The Renaissance changed the way Europeans thought about themselves and the world, paving the way for exploration and discovery.	Better maps, ships and instruments, such as the compass and astrolabe, improved sea travel.

2. Statement: Spain and Portugal had several reasons for wanting to find a sea route to Asia.

Portugal did not have a Mediterranean port, so it needed another way to trade with Asia.	The Portuguese wanted to find a more direct way to trade for West African gold	Spain wanted the riches of trade with Asia, and Spain's queen wanted to use sea travel to spread Christianity.

3. Statement: Spain's conquests affected the economic and social development of the Americas.

Spanish conquistadors destroyed the Aztec and Inca Empires.	The Spanish introduced animals, such as horses, to the Americas. They also brought new diseases that cost many lives.	A class system was developed with mestizos, Native Americans, and enslaved Africans at the bottom.

4. Statement: European nations established colonies in North America for several reasons.

Nations wanted to increase their wealth by establishing colonies that could provide them with gold, silver, raw materials, and furs.	Europeans wanted to teach and convert Native Americans to Christianity.	European nations could sell goods to their colonies.

Reteaching Activity

1. Christopher Columbus
2. John Cabot
3. Amerigo Vespucci
4. Juan Ponce de León
5. Ferdinand Magellan
6. Hernán Cortés
7. Francisco Pizarro
8. Jacques Cartier
9. Hernando de Soto
10. Samuel de Champlain
11. Henry Hudson

Guided Reading Activity

A Changing World

I. A. Crusades
   B. spices
   C. classical, Renaissance
   D. monarchs
II. A. maps
   B. astrolabes, compasses
   C. caravel
III. A. taxes
   B. Timbuktu
   C. Quran

Answer Key

Early Exploration

1. F. Bartholomeu Dias discovered the Cape of Good Hope.
2. T.
3. F. Following Cabral's voyage, Portugal established its first permanent forts in India.
4. T.
5. F. Columbus found a sponsor in Spain to finance his voyage.
6. F. Columbus thought he had reached the East Indies in 1492, but instead he had reached the Americas.
7. T.

Spain in America

1. The conquistadors received grants that gave them the right to explore and establish settlements in the Americas.
2. Spain gained control of land in present-day Mexico.
3. Francisco Pizarro gained control of the Inca Empire.
4. The Spanish arrived with weapons and animals new to the Aztec and Inca; Native Americans who disliked their overlords helped the Spanish; the Aztec and Inca were victims of European diseases, which weakened their resistance.
5. Ponce de León landed on the east coast of present-day Florida in 1513.
6. Tales of seven cities of gold inspired de Soto's expedition.

   A mission is a religious community that usually includes a small town, surrounding farmland, and a church.
7. The giving of encomienda turned Native Americans into slaves.
8. The plantation system brought slave labor to the colonies.

Exploring North America

1. Protestant Reformation
2. Martin Luther
3. mercantilism
4. resources
5. Columbian Exchange
6. Northwest Passage
7. John Cabot
8. Jacques Cartier
9. Henry Hudson
10. fur trading
11. coureurs de bois
12. New Netherland

Colonial America

Content Vocabulary Activity

1. burgesses
2. Mayflower Compact
3. patroon
4. indentured servant
5. charters
6. Pilgrims
7. pacifists
8. debtors
9. headright
10. dissent
11. tenant farmer
12. proprietary colony
13. joint-stock company
14. Puritan
15. Fundamental Orders of Connecticut
16. constitution
17. Separatist
18. mission

Academic Vocabulary Activity

A. Word Meaning

1. condense
2. colony
3. structural
4. swim
5. legal document

Answer Key

B. Word Usage

1. ethnicities
2. expanded
3. policy
4. functioned
5. estates

Primary Source Readings

1. The Spaniards tried to fence the buffalo in a corral.
2. The author uses descriptions of cows, goats, hogs and mules to explain the buffalo.
3. The author discusses the buffalo's shape, head, face, hide, tail, legs, and overall shape.
4. The buffalo looks like a mixed-up version of animals he has already seen.
5. Responses will vary.

Writing Skills Activity

Practicing the Skill

1. B
2. A
3. B
4. A

Applying the Skill

Answers may vary but should illustrate parallel structures. Sample answers:

1. Spanish missions were set up in New Mexico, Texas, California, and other areas of North America.
2. Some enslaved Africans learned trades such as blacksmithing and weaving.
3. Junipero Serra was born in 1713, left Spain in 1749, and established a mission in San Diego in 1769.
4. While most Spanish colonists settled in the Carribbean, Mexico, and Central America, most French and English colonists settled in North America.

Social Studies Skills Activity

Practicing the Skill

1. The subject of this bar graph is the population of the American colonies from 1680 to 1860.
2. The population of the colonies in 1690 was 200,000.
3. The population increased by 100,000 from 1700 to 1710.
4. The biggest increase occurred between 1720 and 1730.

Applying the Skill

Students' answers will vary but should have approximately the same graph patterns and responses to the questions.

Differentiated Instruction Activity

1. The groups of Amish, Mennonite, and Lutheran immigrants who migrated from Germany's Rhine district to southeastern Pennsylvania became known as the "Pennsylvania Dutch."
2. Students' answers will vary. Possible answer: Several of the symbols used in hex signs relate to growth, abundance, and fertility. This is likely because the original Pennsylvania Dutch were farmers who depended on a good crop for their livelihood. Symbols relating to agriculture would therefore have great meaning to them.

Critical Thinking Skills Activity

Practicing the Skill

1. a diary
2. The roads were sometimes very bad. Travelers sometimes had to stumble over fallen trees blocking the road to continue on their journeys. Insects and bad weather bothered travelers, who sometimes used Native Americans as guides.
3. The writer had a Native American guide who knew the area well. The writer

Answer Key

also mentions an old Native American settlement.

4. Answers will vary. Accept all reasonable answers, such as a diary gives firsthand eyewitness information about people, places, and events.

5. The writer might have certain biases, for example, against certain types of people,

that would influence the way he would write about them. Also, the person writes only from his point of view.

Applying the Skill

1. B	**3.** D
2. C	**4.** A

Geography and History Activity

See map for answers 1, 2, 4, 5.

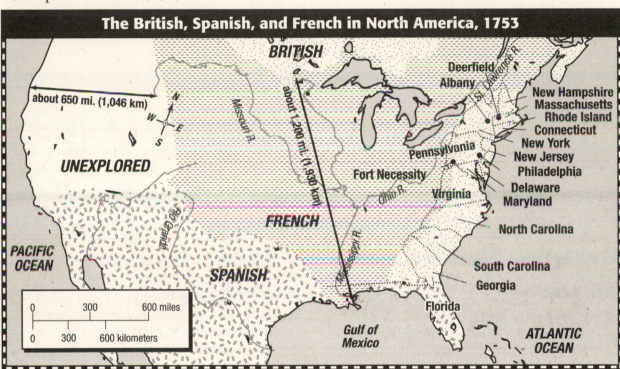

The British, Spanish, and French in North America, 1753

3. Answers may vary: The British were interested in setting up permanent colonies from the start, and hoped to make a big profit. The French were only interested in making a profit from fur trading and fishing, not in setting up colonies. British colonies grew quickly, which created conflicts with Native Americans over land. The French did not have these battles over land because their colonies grew very slowly and Native Americans could stay where they were.

Linking Past and Present Activity

1. Students might find the following information from the U.S. Census Bureau:

1996	179,935,000	105,017,000	58.4
2004	197,005,000	125,736,000	63.8

Answer Key

2. Letters will vary, but students should include logical reasons to support their opinions. Letters should include persuasive arguments that detail why popular rule is important.

Time Line Activity

COLONIAL GOVERNMENTS

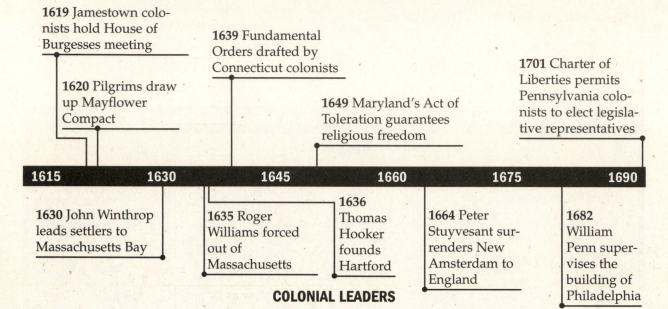

1619 Jamestown colonists hold House of Burgesses meeting

1620 Pilgrims draw up Mayflower Compact

1639 Fundamental Orders drafted by Connecticut colonists

1649 Maryland's Act of Toleration guarantees religious freedom

1701 Charter of Liberties permits Pennsylvania colonists to elect legislative representatives

| 1615 | 1630 | 1645 | 1660 | 1675 | 1690 |

1630 John Winthrop leads settlers to Massachusetts Bay

1635 Roger Williams forced out of Massachusetts

1636 Thomas Hooker founds Hartford

1664 Peter Stuyvesant surrenders New Amsterdam to England

1682 William Penn supervises the building of Philadelphia

COLONIAL LEADERS

School-to-Home Connection Activity

What Do You Know?

Sample answers:

Partner's answer: The "starving time" was the winter of 1609–1610. When John Smith left Jamestown, the town did not have a strong leader to guide it and the people ended up starving.

Student's answer: Roger Williams settled Rhode Island because he believed that people should not be persecuted for their religious beliefs and the government should not tell people how to worship.

Partner's answer: The Charter of Liberties granted colonists the right to elect representatives to the legislature.

Student's answer: "Blue gold" is indigo, a flowering plant used to dye cloth. It became an important crop in Carolina.